What on Earth is Star Wars?

What on Earth is Star Wars?

A Guide to the Strategic Defense Initiative

Frank Barnaby

Fourth Estate · London

First published in Great Britain in 1986 by
Fourth Estate Ltd
Classic House
113 Westbourne Grove
London W2 4UP

Copyright © 1986 Frank Barnaby

British Library Cataloguing in Publication
Data

Barnaby, Frank
    What on earth is Star Wars?: a guide to the
    Strategic Defense Initiative.
    1. Nuclear weapons   2. Weapons systems
    3. Strategy   4. Space warfare
    I. Title
    358'.17   U264

ISBN 0-947795-15-4

Typeset by M.C. Typeset, Chatham, Kent
Printed and bound by Richard Clay Ltd, Bungay, Suffolk

For Sophie and Ben

Contents

Acknowledgements

Ballistic Missile Organisation: 20
Daily Telegraph Colour Library: 17, 18
Department of Defense, Washington: MARS 2, 6, 7, 8, 9, 10, 13, 19
Hughes Aircraft Company: MARS 14
MacClancey Collection: 4, 5
McDonnell Douglas Corporation: 11
NASA: 1, John C. Olson 3
US Air Force: 12, 15, 16

Introduction

Let us turn to the very strengths in technology that spawned our great industrial base and that have given us the quality of life we enjoy today. What if free people could live secure in the knowledge that their security did not rest upon the threat of instant US retaliation to deter a Soviet attack, that we could intercept and destroy strategic ballistic missiles before they reached our own soil or that of our allies? . . . .

I call upon the scientific community in our country, those who gave us nuclear weapons, to turn their great talents now to the cause of mankind and world peace, to give us the means of rendering these nuclear weapons impotent and obsolete.

My fellow Americans, tonight we're launching an effort which holds the promise of changing the course of human history.

President Reagan spoke these words at 8 pm on 28 March 1983, from the Oval Office at the White House; the President defined his ultimate goal as *'eliminating the threat posed by strategic nuclear missiles'*. In other words, the President's vision is the deployment of such effective ballistic missile defences that the whole population of the USA would be protected from an all-out attack by Soviet strategic ballistic missiles. The President has since made it clear that he wants his nuclear umbrella also to cover the populations of America's Western European allies, Canada and Japan.

The concept of a total ballistic missile defence is by

no means new. The subject was thoroughly thrashed out, particularly in the USA in the late 1960s and early 1970s, when the Pentagon tried to get funds for the deployment of anti-ballistic missiles (ABMs) (the term 'ballistic missile defence system' is synonymous with the term 'anti-ballistic missile system'). Pressure from the public and a section of the scientific community, and eventually from the US Congress, persuaded President Nixon to begin negotiations about strategic nuclear weapons with the Soviets in November 1969 in Geneva. While the negotiations were going on, the Americans persuaded the Soviets to accept that a nationwide ballistic missile defence would be futile, dangerous and very expensive.

Senior American scientists played a key role in this process, putting the case against ballistic missile defences to their Soviet colleagues (during, for example, Pugwash Conferences on Science and World Affairs), who in turn influenced Soviet political leaders. The strength of the Soviet belief in the most effective defence, based on horrific experiences of foreign invasions and occupations, made it no easy task to persuade the Soviets to give up the idea of a total ballistic missile defence system. But the effort succeeded and in 1972 the ABM Treaty, prohibiting the deployment of a nationwide ballistic missile defence system, was signed.

Why, then, did both sides conclude in 1972 that total ballistic missile defences are futile, dangerous, and costly? The explanation was aptly given by the US Arms Control Association:

Futile: because in a competition between defensive systems and offensive missiles with nuclear warheads, the offense would win, especially against populations and urban areas. Destabilizing: because the arms race would be accelerated as both sides developed and deployed not only competing ABM systems, but also offsetting systems to overpower, evade, or attack and disable the opposing ABM system. Furthermore, each side would fear the purpose or the capability of the other's ABMs (especially against a weakened retaliatory strike), and in a crisis these fears could bring mounting pressures for striking first. What strategic theorists refer to as arms race instability and crisis instability could both result. Costly: because both ABM development and deployment, and the build-up, modernization and diversification of offsetting offensive forces, must be purchased.

In the 15 years or so since this judgement, considerable progress has been made in the development of high-energy lasers, sophisticated radars and other sensors. And there are now computers that can process rapidly huge amounts of information that may be applicable to ballistic missile defence systems. But are these vast new technological advances a reason for changing the earlier judgement about the feasibility and desirability of total ballistic missile defences? And do ballistic missile defences need to be 'leak-proof'? Is there any point in having ballistic missile defences even if only a very few enemy warheads get through? Another crucial question is: if perfect or near-perfect strategic defences are neither feasible nor desirable, what about setting up partial defences against enemy ballistic missile attack around, for example, intercontinental ballistic missile sites? These questions are some of the most hotly-debated defence issues today; this book will attempt to give the information necessary for the reader to make judgements about this crucial and constantly-changing subject.

The discussion has become completely polarized,

with advocates and critics growing increasingly vehement. Interestingly, some of the most eminent experts such as Richard Garwin, Hans Bethe, Wolfgang Panofsky and Sidney Drell, who all led the campaign against ABMs in the 1960s, are now leading the opposition against the Strategic Defense Initiative with equal vigour.

President Reagan has stated that if his Strategic Defense Initiative, or SDI – essentially a research programme to see which technologies are feasible in a ballistic missile defence system – shows that strategic nuclear defence is possible, then there should be negotiations with the Soviet Union about the deployment of such defences. 'If and when we finally achieve our goal, and that is a weapon that is effective against incoming missiles', the President explained, 'then rather than add to the mistrust in the world and appear to be seeking the potential for a first strike by rushing to implement, my concept has always been that we sit down with the other nuclear powers, our allies and our adversaries, and see if we cannot use that weapon to bring about ... the elimination of nuclear weapons.' But when asked if this meant that the Soviets could veto the US deployment of a nationwide ballistic missile defence system, the President replied 'Hell, no!'. And, he added that if such negotiations failed, 'we would go ahead with deployment'. On this occasion, then, the President said clearly that the unilateral deployment of strategic nuclear defences by the USA was possible. Yet on other occasions, the President has even offered to share Star Wars (as it has come to be known) technologies with the Soviets. But neither he nor any of his officials has really explained what these statements mean in practice.

One thing is clear: An *effective nationwide* ballistic missile defence against an attack by the strategic ballistic missiles of a superpower must involve many weapon systems in space, including a network of satellites and space battle stations. This is why President Reagan's Strategic Defense Initiative has been dubbed 'Star Wars', evoking battle scenes from the famous film. These enormously costly military space assets will be highly vulnerable to attack and will therefore have to be defended in turn. The deployment of such defences will, in effect, lead to the domination of space. This gives new poignancy to President J. F. Kennedy's remark: 'Only if the United States occupies a position of pre-eminence can we help decide whether this new ocean will be a sea of peace, or a terrifying theater of war.' The 'pre-eminence' that Kennedy had in mind was, however, not military domination.

Star Wars could lead to the total militarization of space. But in fact few realize how militarized space has already become. Chapter 1 will describe the military uses of space to date, to set the scene for a description of the much greater militarization of space that would follow if President Reagan's Star Wars vision becomes a reality.

Chapter 1

The Militarization of Space

Weapons in space date back to the Second World War when, on 3 October 1942, the Germans, after about 20 years of research, development and testing, successfully launched the V-2 missile. The V-2, which had a range of about 320 kilometres (200 miles) – enough to hit London from launch sites near Wassenaar, Holland – reached a height of about 100 kilometres (60 miles). No man-made object had previously reached this height; the V-2 qualifies, if only just, as the first man-made object in space.

The success of the V-2 rocket (about 10,000 were produced of which about a half were fired during the war) led the superpowers to develop the first delivery systems for nuclear bombs – intercontinental ballistic missiles (ICBMs) carrying nuclear warheads. These missiles have ranges of 10,000 to 12,000 kilometres (6,250 to 7,500 miles), can reach heights (apogees) of about 1,200 kilometres (750 miles), and typically stay in space for 25 minutes or so. Although most missiles travel through space on a ballistic trajectory similar in shape to the flight path of a stone, some have been designed to stay in space for a longer time. For example, the Soviet Fractional Orbital Bombardment System, or FOBS as it was called, was designed to be fired into space and travel in an orbit that would take it eastwards from the USSR. When the warhead had completed just over half its orbit it would find itself over the USA and, at an appropriate point, the warhead would be fired at its American target. In this way, Soviet warheads could creep in behind the American radar systems that give warning of an enemy missile attack. When these radars were installed, it was assumed that Soviet missiles would come from the east; a FOBS warhead would have approached the USA from the west, a direction in which the American radars would not be looking. The snag with FOBS was that it was inaccurate and, when accuracy became the by-word for the successful delivery of missile warheads, the Soviets abandoned the system.

Military Satellites

The most consistent military activity in space is the use of satellites. Since October 1957, when the space-satellite age was born with the launching into orbit of Sputnik-1, about 2,400 satellites have been launched into space for military purposes. This means that three out of every four satellites put into space are for military use. In a typical year, about 100 military satellites are launched by the superpowers – about 85 by the Soviets and 15 by the Americans. The different numbers actually indicate the superiority of American satellite technology – American satellites usually stay up in space for longer periods. For example, a typical US Big Bird satellite stays in space for about 200 days, whereas a Soviet Cosmos satellite tends to come down after about 30 days.

Many think that the USA and the USSR are the only military powers in space. But China, France, India and Japan are also space powers, having launched their own spacecraft. Other countries also plan to graduate to space powers; Brazil, for example, has advanced high-altitude rocket programmes in which rockets are fired into the upper atmosphere. Membership of the space club is regarded, in today's world, as a major military status symbol. Be that as it may, the USA and the USSR are by far the biggest military users of space. China, the next biggest, has launched a total of only 16 satellites.

Satellites are used by the military for reconnaissance, communications and early warning of ballistic missile attack, as well as for many other functions such as the detection of nuclear explosions, navigation and ocean surveillance.

The most obvious use of military satellites is to spy on the enemy. In fact, espionage, or to use a politer word, reconnaissance, is so important that some 40 per cent of all the military satellites launched are for photographic reconnaissance, of which there are two kinds. One type of satellite scans a large area of territory using a wide-angle, low-resolution camera. If the photographs show something of interest, the second type of reconnaissance satellite, carrying a high-resolution camera, is sent in to have a closer look. The photographs taken by these 'close-look' satellites often show incredible detail – individual soldiers can be seen, for example, and the photographs can even reveal what the soldiers are doing. Increasingly, these two operations – large-area surveillance and close-look – are done by one satellite. The American Big Bird, for example, can do both. Photographic reconnaissance satellites are the 'eyes' of the military in space; electronic reconnaissance satellites – that detect and monitor the enemy's radar signals, his radio communications and even his telephone conversations – are the military's space 'ears'.

Electronic reconnaissance satellites carry the most sophisticated electronic equipment to collect and analyse all the radio signals generated by other countries' military forces. These satellites are relevant to ballistic missile defence systems because part of their job is to collect information about radars used by early-warning-of-attack systems, including those associated with anti-ballistic missile defences.

They also monitor the other side's ballistic missile test flights to obtain information about the characteristics of the missiles being tested.

In fact the US planned to launch a new and very sophisticated electronic intelligence satellite, the KH-12, into orbit in September this year. This satellite could play an important role in an American ballistic missile defence system. The KH-12 is probably too heavy to be launched by an unmanned rocket and can only be put into orbit by the space shuttle; the loss of Challenger will postpone the launch of the KH-12.

Reconnaissance satellites use various types of orbits. Photographic reconnaissance satellites often use relatively low orbits – between 120 and about 2,000 kilometres (75 and 1,250 miles) above the Earth. Electronic satellites usually orbit 600 to 800 kilometres (375 to 500 miles) above the Earth. Vela satellites, designed to detect nuclear explosions in the atmosphere and in outer space, operate in orbits 110,000 kilometres (68,750 miles) above the Earth, way out in space.

The military also use many satellites for communications. It is, in fact, no exaggeration to say that the military has come to rely heavily on its communications satellites; these would also play an important role in future ballistic missile defence systems. They usually operate in geostationary orbits, about 36,000 kilometres (22,500 miles) above the Earth, which means that they revolve around the Earth at a speed that keeps them at the same point above the equator. A satellite in a geostationary orbit 'looks', therefore, at the same area of the Earth all the time.

A typical communications satellite's orbiting weight is about 450 kilograms (1,000 pounds), and it is equipped with about 7 square metres (8½ square yards) of silicon solar cells mounted on panels which are kept pointing to the sun. The solar cells produce enough power, typically about 750 watts, to charge the nickel-cadmium batteries carried by the satellite to operate its communications equipment. Some communications satellites, however, would be much larger than this. A Fleet Satellite Communication System (FLTSATCOM) satellite used by the US Navy, for example, weighs about 2 tons.

In April 1983, the US Challenger space shuttle launched into orbit the Tracking and Data Relay Satellite System (TDRSS) – two special satellites in geostationary orbits, communicating with a ground terminal at White Sands, New Mexico. It was this space shuttle that so tragically exploded on launch on 28 January 1986, killing all seven people on board.

TDRSS relays data, commands, and video and voice messages to and from American spacecraft and the ground terminal. The system can service up to 100 separate spacecraft and has considerable military significance inasmuch as it allows virtually continuous communications between Earth and military spacecraft, even when they are on the other side of the Earth.

Also stationed in geostationary orbits are satellites to give early warning of a ballistic missile attack, and these would certainly be crucial to any ballistic missile defence programme. They monitor permanently the areas containing intercontinental ballistic missile silos in, for example, the USSR. If the missiles in these silos were ever fired, infra-red sensors on the satellites would detect the infra-red radiation in the flames of the booster rockets. (Infra-red radiation is electromagnetic radiation, like light, radio waves and X-rays, but of a different wavelength. Emitted by any hot body, it is used by infra-red sensors to detect objects which give off too little visible light to be seen.) Following detection, signals would be sent from the satellites to the military command centre giving warning that enemy missiles were on their way. Other early-warning satellites monitor areas where enemy strategic nuclear submarines may be lurking, to detect any missiles launched from these submarines.

Military navigation satellites would also play a role in ballistic missile defences. The US Global Position Satellite System called NAVSTAR, for example, will use 18 satellites in orbits 17,500 kilometres (11,000 miles) above the Earth. This space-based radio navigation system, which should be fully operational in 1988, will provide extremely accurate data on position, speed and time for civilian ships and aircraft. Using a NAVSTAR receiver any vehicle will be able to determine its position anywhere in the world to a few tens of yards in each of the three dimensions, speed to within a few inches per second and time to a millionth of a second. But NAVSTAR will also send out, in code, even more accurate data for military purposes, including the guidance of, for example, ballistic missile defence weapons.

So satellites are crucial to Star Wars, particularly to give rapid warning when Soviet strategic ballistic missiles have been fired, for the control and management of the space battle, for communications and for the guidance of space weapons. Also crucial to Star Wars will be the use of space shuttles – both to launch heavy satellites into deep space and to construct space battle stations.

Space Shuttles and Space Battle Stations

Sophisticated ballistic missile defences depend on an ability to attack enemy intercontinental ballistic missiles soon after they have been fired out of their silos. This can only be done if the weapons used to attack the missiles (or, as will be seen later, components of these weapons such as mirrors for ground-based lasers) have a direct line of sight to their targets – even Star Wars weapons shoot in straight lines! Because of the curvature of the Earth, much of the Star Wars arsenal will have to be stationed in space on space battle stations. And the construction of these battle stations will require extensive use of space shuttles.

In anticipation of greatly increased space activities, the US Air Force is building a new $1,000-million centre near Colorado Springs, within sight of the Rocky Mountains. The Consolidated Space Operations Center (CSOC) will control and manage American military space operations. The US Air Force is also building its own shuttle launch site at the Vandenberg Air Force Base, from where most US military satellites are now launched. The first shuttle flight from Vandenberg was planned for July 1986. The shuttle was to carry into space some Star Wars components to test them. But the Challenger disaster will almost certainly delay this, and all other shuttle flights, for many months.

It is no coincidence that Colorado Springs is also the home of the North American Air Defense Command (NORAD), with its nerve centre buried deep inside Cheyenne Mountain. NORAD's function is to give early warning of a missile attack on North America and to keep track of the huge number of objects in space. Including satellites (operational and 'dead'), bits of launchers, and other space 'litter', there are currently over 5,000 such objects.

When CSOC is built, the US Air Force Space Command will be able to control US military space shuttle and satellite operations from the same headquarters, and to keep track of all space objects. The most crucial task in a large-scale ballistic missile defence system is firing and controlling the weapons used to intercept and destroy the enemy missiles or their warheads. Because of the shortage of time and the terrific complexity of the task, this 'battle management' would have to be fully automated; there will be no time for human involvement in Star Wars. Colorado Springs is the obvious home for a Star Wars headquarters and is bound to have a substantial role in future ballistic missile defences.

The first American space shuttle, Columbia, was launched on 12 April 1981. Until then, objects were launched into space by rockets that could only be used once. Reusable space shuttles were found to be much more economical, flexible and efficient than rockets and ushered in an important new phase of the space age. Since Columbia, the Americans have developed three other space shuttles – Challenger, Discoverer and Atlantis. Challenger blew up on 28 January 1986; the other three space shuttles are still operating.

A space shuttle consists of the orbiter vehicle that carries the crew and the payload, the external tank, and two solid-fuelled rocket boosters. The cargo – possibly including a military satellite – is carried in a bay 20 metres (22 yards) long and 5 metres (5½ yards) in diameter. A typical shuttle flight in space lasts about seven to thirty days, beginning its journey with the simultaneous ignition of the main engines and booster rockets. At a predetermined point, the two boosters fall away from the orbiters and parachute to the sea; they are recovered and used again. The orbiter continues into space, and just before going into Earth orbit the external tank is dropped off, burning up as it re-enters the atmosphere. Returning from their space missions American shuttles land on a runway at the Kennedy Space Center, or the Vandenberg Air Force Base.

Depending on the orbit chosen, the shuttle can launch a load ranging from 10 to 30 tons into orbits about 600 kilometres (375 miles) high. By comparison the Soviet SL-13, a current Soviet non-reusable space launch rocket, has a launch-weight of about 670 tons and can lift a 20-ton object into an orbit of height 180 klilometres (110 miles). In the next ten years, 500 or so experiments are planned for American space shuttle flights – and about one-third will be for the military. For some of the shuttle's military tasks, the Pentagon will use a booster to carry loads of up to 2.2 tons into very high orbits, including geostationary orbits at heights of 36,000 kilometres (22,500 miles).

The military use space shuttles to place satellites in orbit, snatch them out of orbit and repair and service them in orbit. While performing these tasks, astronauts gain experience in working in space outside their spacecraft; they can carry small rockets so that they can manoeuvre themselves in space without any physical connection with the shuttle orbiter. They will use this invaluable experience to construct space stations.

The Soviets are also experimenting with reusable space vehicles – including a space plane and a space shuttle similar to the American one. Delta-winged re-entry vehicles (space planes) have been launched into space and recovered after spending some time in orbit. On 19 December 1984, for example, Cosmos 1614 was put into an orbit about 220 kilometres (140 miles) high, and recovered from the Black Sea. And Soviet manned flights with a space shuttle are expected soon. The Soviet shuttle will probably be a smaller version of the American one, perhaps weighing about 10 to 15 tons (the American shuttle weighs about 35 tons).

The USSR has been putting men and women in space since 1961, when Yuri Gagarin was the first man to be shot into space. Their manned space missions take place at the rate of three or four a year, and they began building space stations in April 1971 when Salyut 1 was launched, using Soyuz satellites to transfer people and goods between Earth and Salyut space stations. In 1982, two Soviet cosmonauts spent 211 days on space-station Salyut 7. And in 1984, three cosmonauts spent 237 days on the space station, setting a world record. Soviet cosmonauts have chalked up about 4,000 person-days in space, three times the US astronauts' total. But with the frequent use of the space shuttle, American astronauts will quickly accumulate time in space. Within a few years there will probably be hundreds of people in space, many constructing space stations.

The Soviets have started to replace Salyut 7 with a modular space station that will grow into a large space complex, permanently supporting 20 or so cosmonauts. And, in 1984, President Reagan instructed the National Aeronautics and Space Administration (NASA) to develop a permanently-manned space station; Congress agreed and has provided the initial funding for the project. NASA expects to be operating a permanently-manned space station within a decade. These clearly have great potential as full-scale military bases; because they will be essential for Star Wars, their development and deployment will no doubt be speeded up. The building of such an armada of battle stations required for Star Wars will need space shuttles carrying bigger loads of 100 tons or more, so we can expect this type of 'shuttle' to be developed from now on.

Early Developments of US Anti-ballistic Missiles

Proposals for defending the USA against a ballistic missile attack, particularly by Soviet intercontinental ballistic missiles (ICBMs) go back at least 30 years. Soviet interest in ballistic missile defences is as long-standing. The early US proposals provoked a heated debate on strategic missile defences. Today's debate, stimulated by President Reagan's intense and high-profile interest in nuclear defence, has so much in common with the earlier debate that a knowledge of the history of ballistic missile defences is vital in following the current discussions.

The story begins in the early 1950s when both the US Army and the US Air Force commissioned studies to look into the feasibility of intercepting Soviet ICBMs at some distance from their targets. These studies were actually conducted before the deployment of the first Soviet ICBM, which was called the SS-6 Sapwood by NATO authorities. The SS-6 was a massive missile, 30 metres (33 yards) long, 3 metres (10 feet) in diameter and weighing about 300 tons. Incredible though it now seems, 32 rocket engines were used to launch the missile, which could deliver a large thermonuclear warhead (hydrogen bomb) over a range of 10,000 kilometres (6,250 miles) or more. The SS-6 was used mostly to launch satellites into space, including the first Sputnik on 4 October 1957, and the first man in space on 12 April 1961. The SS-6 was tested as an ICBM in August 1957 and may have became operational in 1959 – but this gigantic missile was probably never taken very seriously as an ICBM.

The first standard Soviet ICBM was the SS-7 Saddler, a 100-ton missile capable of delivering a thermonuclear warhead with an enormous explosive power equivalent to that of about 25 million tons of TNT, over a range of about 11,000 kilometres (7,000 miles). The SS-7 became operational in 1961 and remained in service with the Soviet strategic nuclear forces right up to 1980.

The success of early Soviet space activities, particularly the launching into orbit of Sputnik-1, dramatically demonstrated that the USSR could soon deploy an ICBM force. In fact, by the end of the 1950s both superpowers were replacing long-range bombers with ballistic missiles as the main element in their strategic nuclear forces. Attention then switched, particularly in the USA, from anti-aircraft defences to ballistic missile defences.

In January 1958, US Secretary of Defense McElroy decided that the Nike-Zeus system should be developed as an anti-ballistic missile system. This included the Zeus surface-to-air missile and the Zeus Acquisition Radar (ZAR). In the words of Bill Gunston, a leading British missile expert, ZAR looked 'rather like the Great Pyramid and was almost as large' – it was so vast that one of its aerials weighed 1,000 tons.

The first Zeus missile was tested in December 1959. This missile had a launch-weight of about 18 tons, was about 19 metres (21 yards) long and 1.5 metres (16 yards) in diameter, and carried a thermonuclear warhead to an altitude of about 400 kilometres (250 miles). The missile had two booster stages and the warhead was carried by a third-stage motor to guide it to the point of interception with an incoming Soviet warhead. Because the Discrimination Radar involved mechanical scanning (using an aerial rotated by a motor like the familiar radar aerials often seen on airports), it soon became clear that it was far too slow for use in a ballistic missile defence system against the rapidly growing Soviet ICBM force. In fact, the whole Nike-Zeus system was too primitive to meet the challenge.

The Pentagon concluded that larger and faster computers, more sophisticated radars and a new missile with a very high acceleration were needed. The idea was to deploy a ballistic missile defence having two layers. Enemy warheads would first be intercepted outside the Earth's atmosphere by missiles with a range of about 700 kilometres (450 miles).

The enemy warheads that survived the first layer of defence would be attacked with the high-acceleration missiles within the Earth's atmosphere at ranges of up to about 40 kilometres (25 miles).

In the context of the current Star Wars debate it is interesting to discover that some of the schemes considered for ballistic missile defence in the early 1960s included a number of space-based systems. For example, one planned to have 12 satellites in Earth orbits to eject clouds of small metal pellets (like ball-bearings) into the path of enemy warheads. Collision with the pellets would damage the warheads enough to disable them.

Because of its limitations, President Eisenhower decided to cancel the Nike-Zeus system in 1959. But in 1963, President Kennedy – who aptly described ballistic missile defence as 'hitting a bullet with another bullet' – authorized a research and development programme for a new system, called Nike X. The system, which was ground-based, consisted of two interceptor missiles called Sprint and Spartan, plus two new sophisticated radars – the Perimeter Acquisition Radar (PAR) and the Multi-function Array Radar (MAR); the latter being superseded later by the Missile Site Radar (MSR). The two-layered Nike X system demanded considerable advances in radar technology, nuclear-warhead design and missile engineering.

The greatest effort went into developing the giant radars needed to give an adequate early warning of a ballistic missile attack. Ballistic Missile Early Warning System (BWEWS) radar sites were established in Greenland (at Thule), in England (at Fylingdales) and in Alaska, to complement the Perimeter Acquisition Radar at the Grand Forks Air Force Base in North Dakota. These sites are still in operation; their radars and associated computers have been continually modernized.

Today, the ground-based radar network includes radars operating on the East and West coasts of the USA. Continuously monitoring the oceans where Soviet strategic nuclear submarines operate, the radar network provides early warning of attack by submarine-launched ballistic missiles. It also complements a set of early-warning satellites in orbits, enabling them to observe the areas in the USSR where Soviets ICBMs are deployed. These satellites are designed to detect Soviet ICBMs almost immediately after they have been fired.

The first layer of the Nike X ballistic missile defence system, which would intercept attacking Soviet warheads outside the atmosphere, included the Spartan missile, evolved from the Nike-Zeus missile. Spartan was designed to carry a thermonuclear warhead close enough to an incoming Soviet warhead so that the ensuing nuclear explosion and emission of X-rays would destroy the enemy warhead. The Spartan warhead was detonated, at the appropriate moment, by a signal sent by a computer on the ground; the signal was supposed to be sent only when Spartan was close to a real warhead and to ignore decoys. Spartan – 17 metres (56 feet) long, one metre (3¼ feet) in diameter and weighing about 13 tons – had three propulsion stages which could boost the warhead over a distance of about 750 kilometres (470 miles) at an average speed of about 10,000 kilometres (6,250 miles) an hour.

The second layer of defence – the interception in the Earth's atmosphere of enemy warheads that leaked through the first layer – was provided by the Sprint missile. Sprint was cone-shaped, 8 metres (26 feet) long, with a base diameter of 1.4 metres (1½ yards), the whole thing weighing about 3.5 tons. It had an acceleration far exceeding that of any other missile known. It could reach an altitude of about 40 kilometres (25 miles) in a few seconds, carrying a nuclear warhead with an explosive power equivalent to that of a few thousand tons of TNT. Whereas the Spartan warhead was designed to destroy an enemy warhead by irradiating it with X-rays, the Sprint warhead was intended to use mainly neutron radiation to put the warhead out of action. Because the Sprint warhead would be detonated within the atmosphere, neutrons would be best able to penetrate the air and reach the enemy warhead. (X-rays are absorbed by the atmosphere to a much greater extent than neutrons and would therefore not be suited to disabling the second wave of missiles.) At the time, the development of the Sprint warhead was one of the most difficult parts of the ballistic missile defence programme.

In September 1967, President Johnson decided that America should have a ballistic missile defence system, although it was not until 1971 that Spartan and Sprint missiles were shown to be able to intercept warheads with any reliability. The system favoured by the Johnson Administration, called Sentinel, was a 'thin' deployment, meant chiefly to defend some major cities in the USA against a possible nuclear missile attack by China rather than a Soviet attack. This decision, announced on 18 September 1967 in a speech in San Francisco by the then US Secretary of Defense Robert McNamara, was a strange one. In the first place, the Chinese nuclear threat against the USA was virtually non-existent in 1967. There were, however, powerful vested interests (bureaucratic, military and industrial) in favour of deploying ballistic missile defences. McNamara hinted at these when in his speech he used his famous phrase 'the mad momentum of the nuclear arms race'. The Sentinel decision may therefore have been an attempt to appease these interests without opting for a full-scale deployment.

The plan to deploy Sprint and Spartan missiles

close to cities caused a great uproar from US citizens who did not want nuclear-tipped missiles in their back yard. Moreover, a significant fraction of the American scientific community criticized Sentinel harshly on technical grounds. Because of this public and scientific opposition to Sentinel, President Nixon decided to reassess the entire ballistic missile defence programme when he came into office in January 1969. On 14 March of that year the Nixon Administration set about modifying the Sentinel system. Instead of defending cities against an attack by Chinese nuclear missiles, the plan was to defend American ICBM silo installations against an attack by Soviet ICBMs. Although this involved a ballistic missile defence system of roughly the same size and cost (about $6,000 million in 1969 dollars) the name was changed (largely for reasons of domestic public relations) from Sentinel to Safeguard. The change from city defence to silo defence was mainly to reduce public and scientific opposition, but there was a very significant strategic reason – a response to the deployment of the Soviet SS-9 ICBM.

During the 1967 November military parade through Moscow's Red Square, Western military attachés were awestruck by some huge missiles, transported in the parade on large trailers. The Soviets were showing off their new ICBM for the first time in public. It became called the SS-9 Scarp by NATO. The deployment of SS-9 had actually begun in 1966. The 36-metre (40-yard)-long missile had a launch weight of nearly 200 tons, and was powerful enough to carry a warhead with an explosive power equivalent to that of 25 million tons of TNT over a range of about 12,000 kilometres (7,500 miles). By the early 1970s, 288 SS-9s had been deployed; in the mid-1970s they were replaced by the SS-18.

The deployment of the SS-9 frightened the Americans. They believed that the warhead, the most powerful ever deployed as a single operational missile warhead, would be capable of destroying American ICBMs in their silos. The Pentagon argued, therefore, that ballistic missile defences were needed to protect its own ICBMs, particularly the Minuteman missiles, against a sudden Soviet attack. Silo defence also suited that peculiar logic of nuclear deterrence by mutual assured destruction (known as MAD), the policy introduced by McNamara when he was Secretary of Defense. This logic argued that defending cities as the hostages to nuclear deterrence was bad, because it took away these 'hostages', whereas defending ICBM silos was good because it maintained the value of American retaliatory forces by making them less vulnerable to a Soviet pre-emptive attack, thereby increasing the mutual threat of total destruction. In other words, Sentinel would 'destabilize' the nuclear deterrence of mutual assured destruction, while Safeguard would strengthen nuclear deterrence.

In any case Safeguard was more attractive than Sentinel, because its mission was much simpler. An effective city defence (the aim of Sentinel) has to be perfect – or very nearly perfect. Cities are easily destroyed; they are, in the military expert's jargon, 'soft' targets. One large warhead exploded above a city will destroy just about all of it. Only a few warheads have to leak through to make a city defence useless. If you are going to defend cities it only makes sense if you defend *all* major cities; if you are going to defend silos, however, you only need to defend some silos. And only a few ICBMs need survive a surprise attack to provide a credible retaliatory force.

Nevertheless, the Safeguard system was heavily criticized – particularly by some scientists. In the words of one of the main critics, Safeguard 'remained a layered, area-defense system, and as such could not be confined unambiguously to a silo-defense role. Any deployment of the system would have to be regarded by the Soviet Union as the potential base of a future population defense; some of the support for Safeguard actually derived from a similar view.' Safeguard would, it was said, stimulate the nuclear arms race as much as Sentinel.

The critics of ballistic missile defences almost succeeded in stopping the Safeguard programme. In August 1969 the US Congress voted on the request for funds to begin production of the components for Safeguard, even though at this time neither Spartan nor Sprint missiles had completed their testing programmes. The Congressmen were subjected to a great deal of lobbying for and against Safeguard and the result of the vote was a tie – 50 for and 50 against. Vice-President Spiro Agnew kept the system alive by casting his vote in favour of it.

In November 1969, the USA and the USSR began bilateral negotiations in Geneva on limiting strategic nuclear weapons – the so-called Strategic Arms Limitation Talks (SALT). As often happens in these circumstances, officials of the Nixon Administration, particularly Henry Kissinger, argued that the Safeguard ballistic missile defence system should be used as a 'bargaining chip' in the negotiations. The bargaining-chip theory was based on the Soviets knowing that the USA would go ahead and deploy ballistic missile defences if no SALT Treaty was negotiated – and that this would therefore encourage the Soviets to agree to a treaty. On the other hand, it was argued that if the Americans decided to abandon Safeguard, the Soviets would be less motivated to negotiate a SALT treaty.

The ABM Treaty

As it turned out, the Geneva talks led to two agreements – a treaty between the USA and the USSR on the limitation of anti-ballistic missile systems (usually called the ABM Treaty) and an Interim Agreement between the USA and the USSR on certain measures to limit strategic offensive weapons (usually called the SALT I Treaty). Both treaties entered into force on 3 October 1972. The SALT I Treaty froze the number of fixed land-based ICBM launchers and the number of ballistic missile launchers on modern submarines deployed by each superpower. The treaty was in force for five years. The ABM Treaty, and a Protocol to the Treaty which came into force on 25 May 1976, prohibits the deployment of ABM systems for the defence of the *whole territory of the USA and the USSR* but permits the deployment of ABMs around just one area in each country – either for the defence of each national capital, Washington DC and Moscow, or for the defence of one ICBM complex each.

The ABM Treaty, and to a much lesser extent the SALT I Treaty, was a sincere Soviet and American effort to slow down the nuclear arms race between the two superpowers. The treaty was designed to prevent an open-ended acceleration of the arms race, as each side had reacted to the other side's deployment of ABM systems by increasing the number of its own offensive strategic nuclear weapons to saturate the other side's ABM defences. The ABM Treaty was also meant to strengthen the policy of nuclear deterrence by mutual assured destruction; as shown earlier, this brake would have been threatened by the deployment of ballistic missile defences to protect cities. But despite limiting the quantitative increase in the number of nuclear weapons in the Soviet and American arsenals, the ABM and SALT I Treaties totally failed to prevent the next qualitative round of the nuclear arms race from occurring – namely, the improvement in the quality of strategic nuclear missiles by the development and deployment of Multiple Independently-targetable Re-entry Vehicles (MIRVs).

MIRVs increase the number of warheads that can be carried by ballistic missiles. A single missile of this kind is equipped with several re-entry vehicles, each carrying a nuclear warhead. Each MIRV can guide its warhead to a separate target, and the targets covered by the MIRVs can be hundreds of kilometres apart. Clearly, MIRVs greatly increase the effectiveness of strategic ballistic missiles; before their development, a ballistic missile carried just one warhead.

MIRVs were developed in the USA during the 1960s, mainly to overcome the then-anticipated Soviet ABM systems by saturating them with many more warheads so that at least some would penetrate Soviet defences. The negotiation of the ABM Treaty removed the main rationale for MIRVs, but they were not mentioned in the SALT I Treaty because large vested interests, military and industrial, had grown in favour of keeping them. The SALT I Treaty limits the number of launchers of strategic missiles on both sides – but says nothing about the number of warheads each missile can carry.

The USA lost a valuable opportunity here, because after a few years the Soviet Union caught up with the USA in MIRV technology and, as a consequence, Soviet ICBMs became a serious threat to American ICBMs. Because of American shortsightedness in not negotiating MIRVs away in the early 1970s, the Soviets went ahead with the new system and were eventually able to increase considerably the numbers of warheads on their missiles. These are generally much larger than their American counterparts, so that each missile can carry more warheads.

The Development of Soviet Ballistic Missile Defences

Soviet interest in ballistic missile defences, as with the Americans, dates back to the 1950s. But whereas the Americans began with the idea of protecting cities from enemy missile attack and then switched to the protection of ICBM silos (and have now switched back to the defence of city populations) the Soviets have consistently favoured city defence. Thus they chose to deploy ABMs around Moscow as the one site allowed them under the ABM Treaty. (They actually began constructing ABM sites in areas around Moscow in the late 1960s and decided to continue with this, subject to the provisions of the treaty.) The Americans in fact scrapped their Safeguard ABM system in 1975 and have since concentrated on research. The Soviets, however, stayed with ABM deployment and have continued to deploy and modernize the system around Moscow.

The Soviet system is based on an anti-ballistic missile which NATO calls the ABM-1B Galosh. Galosh was first seen in public in the November 1964 military parade through Red Square. The Soviet master of ceremonies described it as 'an interceptor missile'. Few details of this missile could be seen because it was transported in a tubular container; all that was visible, through the open end of the container, were the four nozzles at the back of the first stage of the missile. It is thought that the container is simply mounted vertically and used as the launcher for the missile. The missile's fins would then unfold after it has been fired from the container.

Like all Soviet missiles, Galosh is very large for its class. It is about 20 metres (22 yards) long, about 2.6 metres (8⅔ feet) in diameter (with its fins folded) and weighs about 33 tons. Three rocket stages carry a thermonuclear warhead over a range usually reported to be about 330 kilometres (200 miles), but which may be more. Galosh would intercept an American warhead outside the Earth's atmosphere. The explosive power of the warhead is said to be equivalent to that of 2 or 3 million tons of TNT and if this were exploded in the atmosphere it would do almost as much damage to a built-up area beneath the explosion as would an attacking American warhead!

Galosh is of the same vintage as the American Nike-Zeus missile and its performance is almost certainly comparable. In fact, the ABM system around Moscow – which consists of just one layer of ballistic missile defence – is very similar to the Nike-Zeus system abandoned by the Americans in the 1960s. In the words of John Pike, an American expert on Soviet ABMs: 'The use of mechanically-steered radars and high-yield nuclear warheads substantially limits the effectiveness of this system, which could be easily saturated by even a small attack.'

The original Moscow ABM system consisted of 64 launchers for Galosh missiles at four sites around Moscow. The launchers are probably reloadable, though the loading process would have taken a long time; they are above ground and not in underground silos. At each Galosh site there are six guidance radars called Try Add, including Chekhov target trackers. Two other target-tracking radars called Dog House and Cat House operate from sites south of Moscow and supply information to the Galosh missiles. These radars are old: Dog House, for example, became operational in about 1968. According to Bill Gunston, it has a range of about 2,800 kilometres (1,750 miles). Each of the four ABM sites has its own large computer facility.

The exact purpose of Moscow's ballistic missile defences is not clear. The system is far too primitive to protect a large city and is meant presumably to offer some protection in a nuclear war for that part of the political and military leadership seated in Moscow. But perhaps a more likely reason why the Soviets persisted in deploying a limited ABM system after the ABM Treaty came into force is that strong vested interests, military and bureaucratic, insisted that this be done. The fact that the Soviet people are obsessional about strong defences after so many invasions from the West makes it virtually impossible for political leaders to argue against any defence system.

In 1980 the Soviets began to modernize and expand Moscow's ballistic missile defences. They are now deploying a two-layer system consisting of a new version of the Galosh missile, designed to intercept American warheads outside the Earth's atmosphere, and a high-acceleration anti-ballistic missile to attack, within the Earth's atmosphere, American warheads that get through the first layer of defence. Both types of missile are being deployed in underground silos. It is also reported that the number of ABM launchers will be increased to 100, the number allowed by the ABM Treaty. According to US Intelligence sources, the first new launchers probably became operational at the end of 1985 and the new system could be completed by 1987.

Flight testing of the new version of the Galosh, called the SH-4, was reported in 1976. The missile is smaller than the massive Galosh and may have a more modern lower-yield nuclear warhead, perhaps using neutrons to destroy enemy warheads. The high-acceleration missile, called the SH-8, probably has a range of about 80 kilometres (50 miles), and would therefore require a low-yield warhead also relying on neutrons.

Radars associated with the ABM missiles are also being modernized. Generally, more phased-array radars are being deployed to improve on the old radar installations. Battle management will be provided by a new large phased-array radar at Pushkino, north of Moscow, designed to control interceptions of American warheads. This is a huge radar the size of an Egyptian pyramid, with sides 160 metres (530 feet) long and a height of 40 metres (130 feet). The Soviet system for detecting and tracking an American missile attack consists of a set of early-warning satellites with sensors to detect the infra-red radiation in the flames of the American booster rockets, radars that can detect objects at distances further than the horizon (called Over-The-Horizon, or OTH, radars), and a series of phased-array radars.

American sources tell us that two Soviet OTH radars are directed at US ICBM fields to complement the information received from early-warning satellites. The early-warning system would give about 30 minutes' warning of an American ICBM attack. In addition to the early-warning system, the Soviets have deployed 11 Hen House radars at six locations on the periphery of the Soviet Union to determine the trajectory of attacking ICBMs and feed information to the anti-ballistic missiles around Moscow. The Soviets are said to be building a network of six new large phased-array radars that can track attacking ballistic missiles more accurately than the existing Hen House radar network. Five of these new radars simply enhance the coverage of the old Hen House radars. But the sixth, under construction near Krasnoyarsk in Central Siberia (which happens to be the birth-place of President Brezhnev), is controversial.

According to the Pentagon, the Krasnoyarsk radar 'closes the final gap in the Soviet early-warning radar coverage against ballistic missile attack. Together, the six new large phased-array radars form an arc of coverage from the Kola Peninsula in the north west

Soviet Union, around Siberia, to the Caucasus in the south west'. And, say the Americans, the Krasnoyarsk radar is a blatant breach of the ABM Treaty – because Krasnoyarsk is not within a 150-kilometre (94-mile) radius of Moscow *nor* is it on the periphery of the USSR and pointed outward – the conditions stipulated by the ABM Treaty for early-warning radars. Krasnoyarsk is 3,700 kilometres (2,300 miles) from Moscow and 750 kilometres (470 miles) from the nearest border. The radar is oriented across some 4,000 kilometres (2,500 miles) of Soviet territory to the north east.

The Soviets deny that the Krasnoyarsk radar is for ballistic missile defence; it will, they say, be used for tracking objects in space orbits. And so the Soviet and American controversy about this radar rages on, very much in public, as part of the propaganda war still going on between the superpowers in spite of the apparently relaxed atmosphere at the Gorbachev–Reagan Geneva summit.

As a countercharge to the American allegations of Soviet violation of the ABM Treaty, the Soviets claim that the Americans are doing the same by building similar systems such as the new phased-array radars at Fylingdales in England and by planning such a system for Thule in Greenland, to update the performance of America's ballistic missile early-warning system. We will stop constructing our radar at Krasnoyarsk, say the Soviets, if you, the Americans, stop building your new radar at Fylingdales. After all, the Soviets argue, the performance of the two radars is about the same. The Soviet offer was rejected by the Americans, who argue that the Fylingdales radar is permissible because it was in existence for early-warning purposes before the ABM Treaty was negotiated, and is therefore not covered by the treaty. The important point however is that technically the Fylingdales phased-array radar

41

could, by simply changing the computer software, become integrated into a nationwide American Star Wars ballistic missile defence system, and indeed the Krasnoyarsk radar could in the future be similarly integrated into a nationwide Soviet ABM system. And a nationwide ABM system is just what the ABM Treaty was designed to prohibit.

The Soviet Union, in keeping with its obsession with all types of defence systems, has also deployed very large strategic and tactical defences against attacking aircraft. The Americans, on the other hand, decided long ago that the threat to the USA from long-range Soviet bombers was not big enough to justify large air-defence systems.

Currently, the USSR has nearly 10,000 surface-to-air missile launchers for strategic air defence at over 1,200 sites. Two types of Soviet surface-to-air missiles, the SA-10 and the SA-X-12, have according to the Pentagon 'the potential to intercept some types of strategic ballistic missiles' as well as the capability to intercept tactical ballistic missiles (like the American Lance and Pershing ground-to-ground missiles). Other experts, such as the American John Pike, argue that the SA-10 is probably intended to intercept low-flying cruise missiles rather than ballistic missiles. And, says Pike, the limited acceleration and manoeuvrability of the SA-X-12, which the Soviets are now flight-testing, make it of little use for the interception of ICBMs but 'if, as is expected, the SA-[X-]12 were deployed with a nuclear warhead . . . it could have the capability to intercept some types of long-range ballistic missiles such as SLBMs'.

Some American officials maintain that some SA-X-12 tests have violated the ABM Treaty, which prohibits the testing of surface-to-air missile components in an ABM mode 'by conducting tests involving the use of air defence radars in ABM-related testing activities'. Other officials deny this. For example, a senior Pentagon official, Franklin Miller, described the SA-X-12 as having a capability to intercept tactical (i.e. short-range) ballistic missiles but added that 'there is nothing in its development that contravenes the ABM Treaty because that treaty deals with strategic anti-ballistic missile systems'.

Judging by the ABM systems that the Soviets have deployed, it is clear that the Soviets are considerably behind the Americans in these technologies. Even the modernized ABM system now being deployed around Moscow is little, if any, better than the American Safeguard system, abandoned by the Americans more than a decade ago.

Like the Americans, the Soviets have had for a number of years a substantial research programme into advanced ballistic missile defence technologies. According to the Pentagon, the Soviet's laser programme, for example, is much larger than the American one and 'involves over 10,000 scientists and engineers and more than a half dozen major research and development facilities and test ranges'. Figures like these are, however, not as impressive as they sound; Soviet scientists work much less efficiently than their American counterparts. Nevertheless, the Pentagon claims that the facilities at the Sary Shagan Missile Test Center include 'several air defense lasers, a laser that may be capable of damaging some components of satellites in orbits, and a laser that could be used in feasibility testing for ballistic missile defense applications'. Given the rate at which laser research and development is going ahead in the USA, however, the Americans will soon catch up with the Soviets, if indeed they are behind.

The Soviets have undoubtedly made impressive fundamental discoveries that may well apply to ballistic missile defence systems. For example, they have developed ion sources and radio-frequency quadrupole accelerators for particle beams. These have turned out very effective and are now being used by the Americans in trying to develop particle-beam weapons for Star Wars. And the Soviets were the first to publish papers in the open literature on the X-ray laser, powered by a nuclear explosion. Much of the original work in chemical lasers has also been done by Soviet scientists, particularly at the Sary Shagan Missile Test Center. They have also invented a device that the West has not yet developed – a rocket-driven magneto-hydrodynamic generator producing over 15 million watts of electric power.

The Soviets, however, have major weaknesses in competing with the Americans in ballistic missile defences, particularly in microelectronics and computer technology, and in the development of sensitive sensors. These are critical technologies for detecting and tracking attacking ballistic missiles and their warheads. The ability to collect and process rapidly large amounts of data is crucial for ballistic missile defences. This can only be done by microprocessors, another field in which the Americans are well ahead of the USSR. A second major weakness is that, although renowned in fundamental and theoretical science, the Soviets are not good at technologically exploiting the results of their research; the Americans always tend to do better in the engineering phase of weapons development.

Anti-satellite Warfare

Anti-satellite warfare and ballistic missile defence are very closely related – Siamese twins, so to speak. This is so because of the need to protect the space assets – including satellites, space battle stations, mirrors, and so on – which are so crucial to ballistic missile defence as it is now often envisaged. As soon as these assets are deployed, the other side will obviously plan to attack them; many of their counter-measures will, in turn, rely on satellites.

The enemy's countermeasures will certainly include weapons to attack those satellites involved in the ballistic missile defences threatening their strategic nuclear forces. In turn, the side with the ballistic missile defence system will deploy weapons to attack the other side's satellites to frustrate their countermeasures. The deployment of ballistic missile defences by one side will, in other words, provoke the other side into deploying anti-satellite weapons as a countermeasure and this knowledge will ensure that anti-satellite weapons will be deployed with the ballistic missile defences as a counter-counter-measure. The inevitability of this action-reaction process is one reason why critics of Star Wars warn that it will, in all probability, provoke an unprecedented, open-ended arms race in space, leading to the complete militarization of space.

Anti-satellite warfare and ballistic missile defence are very closely related activities for another reason. Any weapon that can be used to attack an enemy ballistic missile or its warheads can also be used to attack his satellites. Such a weapon may be said to be defensive in a ballistic missile defence system, but it will also most certainly be seen as offensive because of its anti-satellite capability.

As described earlier, both the Soviet and American military rely on the use of satellites for a variety of tasks, although the American military reliance is stronger. If they lost their satellites the military would become, as it were, more or less powerless. Therefore it is hardly surprising that for some time now there has been interest in weapons that can destroy the other side's satellites. Most significantly, anti-satellite warfare is an essential component of a nuclear first strike. The first thing that would be done in such an event would be an attack 'out of the blue' on the other side's satellites.

Soviet Anti-Satellite Warfare Activities

Soviet anti-satellite warfare activities date back to the 1960s, when they first deployed anti-satellite weapons. A typical Soviet anti-satellite weapon is, in fact, another satellite called a hunter-killer or interceptor satellite. The hunter-killer is launched into an orbit that will take it close to the enemy satellite that is its target. When the Soviet hunter-killer is at its closest point to the target it explodes and destroys the enemy satellite. In one version, the hunter-killer satellite shoots out a cloud of small metal pellets into the path of the enemy satellite, probably disabling it.

On 18 June 1982 the Soviet satellite Cosmos 1379 was launched from the space-launch centre at Tyuratam in Kazakhstan. Cosmos 1379 was a hunter-killer. Its mission – to seek out, attack and destroy Cosmos 1375. The target satellite had been launched into orbit from Plesetsk 12 days earlier.

The hunter-killer stalked and intercepted its prey during its second orbit of the Earth. It was manoeuvred towards its target by signals from the Soviet Space Command Centre on the ground in the USSR. The hunter-killer then used its own on-board optical and infra-red sensors to make the final approach; when Cosmos 1379 got close to its target, the killer satellite received a signal from the command centre. The rest of the story is an anticlimax. Cosmos 1379 turned round, headed back towards Earth and burnt up as it re-entered the Earth's atmosphere. Cosmos 1375 went on its merry way.

From the Soviet point of view, however, the test was a success (although rumours from American sources said that the hunter-killer's sensors failed at the crucial moment). If the signal from the command centre had instructed it to, Cosmos 1379 would have exploded and destroyed the target satellite. This is what would have happened in a war. In other Soviet anti-satellite weapon tests, the interceptor satellites were exploded with conventional explosives to test their capability to destroy enemy satellites. These experiments proved the point; there is no purpose in blowing up expensive target satellites unnecessarily when they can go on to do other jobs.

Since 1968, when the Soviets started testing their anti-satellite weapon system, 20 tests have been made. The last one was on 18 June 1982. The Soviets then unilaterally announced a moratorium on further testing, although, in rather typical style, they have never officially admitted to having an anti-satellite weapon programme!

The Soviet hunter-killer satellite is an obsolete and cumbersome affair. The interceptor weighs nearly 3 tons and is launched from an ICBM silo. Up to 1982, SS-9 ICBMs were used to put the hunter-killer into orbit, but these missiles have now been retired. It is doubtful if Soviet hunter-killer satellites could be launched from existing operational ICBM silos and there are conflicting reports about the maximum height the Soviet hunter-killer can reach. The Pentagon claims that 'the interceptor can reach targets orbiting at more than 5,000 kilometres [3,125 miles], but', the Pentagon admits, 'it probably is intended for high-priority satellites at lower altitudes'. The Pentagon does not, however, say what these 'high-priority satellites' in low orbits are likely to be. According to the American Union of Concerned Scientists, the highest altitude reached by a Soviet hunter-killer is about 2,300 kilometres (1,400 miles), although the highest interception apparently took place at about 1,700 kilometres (1,000 miles).

The Soviet hunter-killer is not only cumbersome, it is very slow. As the union of Concerned Scientists points out, 'Since the Soviet anti-satellite system is

47

ground-based, it can only attack a satellite whose ground track (the projection of the orbit onto the Earth's surface) runs close to the launch site. Because of the earth's rotation, this occurs twice a day, so the anti-satellite weapon must wait some six hours on average to attack a particular target satellite.'

The Soviet anti-satellite system is also unreliable. Of the 20 tests so far made, 11 have failed. Experts estimate that the Soviets would take well over a week to destroy all the US satellites that are within range of their anti-satellite weapons! And, remember, US satellites at altitudes greater than 2,300 kilometres (1,400 miles), or in highly elliptical orbits, would be out of range of current Soviet anti-satellite weapons. In fact, about the only American military satellites threatened by the existing Soviet anti-satellite system are reconnaissance satellites in low polar orbits. Crucial communications and early-warning-of-attack satellites would in no way be threatened. In view of this many experts believe that the Soviet system is aimed at Chinese rather than American satellites.

The Pentagon claims that the Soviets are operating a ground-based, high-energy laser at Sary Shagan Missile Test Center which has the capability of 'damaging some components of satellites in orbit'. This is, of course, not an operational anti-satellite weapon. However, the Pentagon speculates that the USSR could, in the late 1980s, 'have prototype space-based laser weapons for use against satellites. In addition, ongoing Soviet programs have progressed to the point where they could include construction of ground-based laser anti-satellite facilities at operational sites. These could be available by the end of the 1980s and would greatly increase the Soviets' laser anti-satellite capability beyond that currently at their test site at Sary Shagan. They may deploy operational systems of space-based lasers for anti-satellite purposes in the 1990s.' But few other sources believe that the Soviets will make such fast progress in their anti-satellite weapon research.

American Anti-satellite Weapon Developments

We have seen that the primitive Soviet anti-satellite weapon system can only attack American satellites in low orbits. And although the existing American anti-satellite system is more capable than the Soviet one, it is also restricted to attacking satellites in relatively low orbits.

Like the Soviets, the Americans developed an anti-satellite weapon system in the 1960s. Between 1964 and 1968, the US operated a system based on the Thor missile. The missiles, which were deployed on Johnston Island in the Pacific, were equipped with nuclear warheads. Normally, Thor missiles were deployed as intermediate-range ballistic missiles. In this role, they were deployed in England from 1959 to 1965; with ranges of about 3,200 kilometres (2,000 miles), they were aimed at targets in the Soviet Union.

The early American anti-satellite weapon is called a 'direct ascent' system, because instead of going into orbit to stalk its target like the Soviet system, the warheads of the Thor missiles were fired into space directly at enemy satellites. The explosion of the nuclear warheads would destroy any satellites in the vicinity; this direct ascent system also operates more rapidly than an orbital system.

Whereas the Soviets continued developing and testing anti-satellite weapons, the Americans dismantled their system in the late 1960s at the height of the debate about the desirability of anti-ballistic missile systems. The role of anti-satellite weapons became part of the debate. It was argued that satellites stabilized Soviet–American relations. In a crisis, early-warning and reconnaissance satellites are able to confirm that neither side is preparing a surprise attack. This prevents panic. Moreover, it was argued that satellite communication between the superpowers is useful during a conflict and perhaps essential to negotiate an end to any war that might break out between the superpowers. Because satellites are 'good' for crisis stability, confidence-building and conflict resolution, they should, it was argued, not be threatened.

But in the late 1970s, the USA sharply changed its attitude. The new tactics had both a military and a diplomatic component: a programme to develop a satellite interceptor, and simultaneous negotiations towards a treaty that would ban the testing and deployment of anti-satellite weapons. Soviet-American negotiations for a treaty failed during the Carter Administration and were abandoned as soon as President Reagan came into office. The development of an American anti-satellite weapon system was, however, accelerated.

This led to the development of another 'direct ascent' weapon using a small missile, about 5 metres (5½ yards) in length, 45 centimetres (17 inches) in diameter and weighing about 1,200 kilograms (2,650 pounds). The two-stage missile is small enough to be launched into space from a converted F-15 Eagle fighter aircraft flying at a very high altitude, of more than 21 kilometres (13 miles). The missile's warhead, called a Miniature Homing Vehicle (MHV), is a cylinder with a diameter of about 30 centimetres (12 inches) and a weight of about 15 kilograms (33 pounds). The MHV carries an infra-red telescope, including a sensor and computer, to seek out and aim the warhead at an enemy satellite.

Precise details of the orbit of the enemy satellite under attack are determined by American ground-based tracking stations and fed into the missile's computer. This information is used to instruct the missile's inertial guidance system which guides the missile towards the target satellite. After the two booster stages have burnt out, the MHV uses its infra-red telescope to home in on the target. Small jets on the MHV enable it to make the final manoeuvres to the target. The warhead then rams the target satellite at very high speed and destroys it by its kinetic energy. With a direct hit on the target, no explosive device is needed to destroy it.

The US Congress has been reluctant to give the Pentagon money to test this anti-satellite weapon. The first test was, nevertheless, made on 12 January 1984. An F-15 Eagle aircraft launched the missile at a point in space to test the telescope and on-board computer but the missile did not carry the MHV. The first flight of the warhead took place on 13 November 1984. The warhead was not, however, aimed at a target satellite but the infra-red guidance system was tested against a star. An operational test was carried out on 13 September 1985. The target, a low-orbit satellite, was destroyed. The test was controversial; although the Pentagon described the target satellite as 'burned out', physicists who had been using it said that it was still providing them with 'very useful data' about solar activity when the military destroyed it!

On 4 September 1985 the Soviets announced that they would end their two-year moratorium if the Americans went ahead with their tests. Towards the end of 1985, the US Congress stepped in and voted for a moratorium on further American testing of the F-15-launched anti-satellite weapon for as long as the Soviets continue their moratorium on anti-satellite weapon testing. The Pentagon was considerably put out by this Congressional decision – it had planned nine more tests of its weapon.

It is reported that the American anti-satellite weapon, like the Soviet system, can attack enemy satellites at altitudes up to about 2,000 kilometres

(1,250 miles). A rationale for the deployment of the American weapon is to counter the threat from Soviet strategic nuclear submarines operating close to American shores. Ballistic missiles fired from these submarines could reach their targets in the USA very quickly – in minutes rather than the half-hour or so taken by ICBMs fired at American targets from sites in the USSR. Anti-satellite weapons could, it is argued, be used to attack the Soviet satellites in low orbit whose task it is to support Soviet strategic nuclear submarines. Following this rationale, the US Air Force plans to modify about 50 of its F-15 Eagles to carry anti-satellite weapons, and the aircraft will operate from Langley Air Force Base, Virginia and McChord Air Force Base, Washington State. The moratorium on testing will presumably delay the planned American deployment of F-15-launched anti-satellite weapons, perhaps indefinitely.

The American anti-satellite weapon system is much more flexible than the Soviet system. It can, in principle, operate from any major air force base or from aircraft carriers. Global coverage is therefore possible, given enough aircraft. The system is also much quicker than the Soviet system which uses fixed land-based launch sites.

The existing American and Soviet systems are presently limited to attacking enemy satellites in low orbits. Both sides, however, have important military satellites in high orbits, both have early-warning and communications satellites in geostationary orbits at altitudes of 36,000 kilometres (22,500 miles), and the Americans have NAVSTAR satellites at altitudes of about 20,000 kilometres (12,500 miles). To destroy these in a relatively short time would probably require high-energy lasers of the type envisaged for ballistic missile defence. In fact, high-energy lasers could threaten all satellites with rapid destruction.

But this may not be necessary to disable crucial military satellites. The equipment carried by them – particularly sensors and sophisticated electronics – is usually very delicate and could be disabled if the satellite were 'illuminated' with a laser beam of relatively low intensity. The Americans have already suggested, but have not confirmed, that the Soviets may have used their ground-based laser beam at the Sary Shagan Missile Test Center to 'interfere with' American military satellites.

Chapter 2

The Strategic Defense Initiative

Ballistic Missiles

Research into and the development of ballistic missile defence have, at least until recently, concentrated on terminal defence – the interception of enemy warheads just above the Earth's atmosphere, and as they re-enter the atmosphere. This is the task of the Soviet ABM system around Moscow and was the purpose of the American Safeguard system. As we have seen, the terminal defence of all major cities, essential for a total ballistic missile defence, is much more difficult than the defence of military targets, such as ICBM silo sites.

Generally, the anti-ballistic missiles considered up to now for terminal defence carry nuclear warheads so that they only need to come close enough to enemy warheads for the nuclear explosion of the ABM to destroy them. A number of suggestions have been made for non-nuclear methods of intercepting enemy warheads. The US Army, for example, has a programme, called the Homing Overlay Experiment (HOE), to develop non-nuclear warheads for ground-based anti-ballistic missiles. One type of HOE warhead is studded with steel weights and consists of a number of metal ribs, about 2.5 metres (8 feet) long. The ribs are wound round the HOE warhead during flight and unfurl (rather like an umbrella) seconds before the HOE warhead reaches an enemy ballistic missile warhead. The enemy warhead is destroyed by the collision.

On 10 June 1984 a HOE warhead succeeded in

destroying a dummy warhead over the Pacific. The anti-ballistic missile carrying the HOE warhead was fired from the US Kwajalein Missile Range and the target warhead was launched by a ballistic missile fired from the Vandenberg Air Force Base, California. Ground-based radars and infra-red sensors carried in aircraft were used to track the target warhead and guide the HOE warhead to it. The success of this experiment gave considerable encouragement to terminal defence enthusiasts.

But in the past few years, the emphasis of ballistic missile defence research has changed from ground-based terminal defence systems to space-based systems. Even before SDI, research had become increasingly geared to developing the elements of space-based systems. In the USA, for example, the Teal Ruby experiment is meant to develop an infra-red telescope to detect enemy missiles and to aim laser and other ballistic missile defence weapons at them. And the US Defense Advanced Research Project Agency's (DARPA) project Talon Gold uses a laser-radar system to achieve the required accuracy to identify and track enemy warheads and point a laser weapon at them. And the aim of another DARPA project, the Large Optics Demonstration Equipment (LODE), is to develop and test a large mirror to be deployed in space to focus and direct a laser beam onto an enemy warhead.

What President Reagan's initiative has done is to increase greatly the pace of this research. Considerable resources were already being spent on ballistic missile defence research – the US, for example, had spent about $4,000 million on high-energy lasers alone before the President's Star Wars speech; since that event the rate of spending has been greatly increased.

Before discussing the magnitude and feasibility of this massive programme, we must understand the characteristics of a ballistic missile attack – particularly the details of the flight paths of various types of ballistic missiles. The simplest task of a ballistic missile defence is dealing with intercontinental ballistic missiles (ICBMs), either by destroying the missiles themselves or their warheads. Deployed in underground silos and aimed at targets in the home land of the other side, ICBMs are made to travel very long distances, typically 10,000 kilometres (6,250 miles). And because they have long ranges, the warheads take a relatively long time – normally about 30 minutes – to reach their targets. The longer the flight time of a warhead, the greater the possibility of successfully intercepting it.

The flight of an ICBM can be broken down into four parts: the boost phase, the post-boost phase, the mid-course phase and the terminal phase.

The boost phase

In the boost phase the rocket engines of the ICBM burn. The burning fuel shoots out great flames behind the ascending missile, producing the dramatic pictures seen on television during space launches. The time taken for the booster rockets to burn varies from one type of ICBM to another. The Soviet SS-18 ICBM, for example, has two rocket stages that burn for a total of five minutes after launch. When the boosters have used up all their fuel and burn out, the SS-18 has reached an altitude of 400 kilometres (250 miles). The American MX ICBM, however, is boosted for a mere three minutes even though it has three rocket stages, climbing to a height of 200 kilometres (125 miles). During the boost phase each rocket stage falls off as soon as it runs out of fuel. At the end of this phase all that remains is a platform known as the 'bus', carrying the missile's warheads.

The post-boost phase: emptying the bus

A modern ICBM carries several MIRVs, each of which can be aimed at a separate target. The bus releases the MIRVs one by one along different paths to their targets, the coordinates of the targets having been fed into a computer on the bus before the missile is launched. Small rockets called thrusters are fired each time an MIRV is released for a time precisely calculated to change the course of the bus enough to send the warhead along the path of its target. This part of the flight path, during which the MIRVs are released from the bus, is called the post-boost phase.

Both the Soviet SS-18 and the American MX ICBM carry 10 MIRVs. It takes about 11 minutes for the bus of the MX to release all 10 warheads, after which it has reached an altitude of about 1,100 kilometres (625 miles). We do not know the corresponding time and height for the SS-18.

Once released from the bus, each warhead makes for its target along a pure ballistic trajectory; it travels under the force of gravity along a path determined by its velocity and similar in shape to that followed by a stone thrown into the air.

The bus of an ICBM may also carry a number of decoys to complicate the task of ballistic missile defences. Balloons made of plastic impregnated with metal are typical decoys; most left empty, others containing warheads. Another type of decoy, chaff, consists of pieces of metal specially designed to reflect radar waves and confuse the defence. War-heads and decoys present the same appearance to radar and infra-red sensors, so that it is very difficult to distinguish between them.

Ballistic missile defence systems extensively use sensors sensitive to infra-red radiation to detect enemy missiles and warheads. In particular, the flames emitted by the rockets of a ballistic missile during the boost phase give off an enormous amount of infra-red radiation which, as mentioned earlier, is used to detect and track the missile during this part of its flight. Infra-red sensors are, however, of less use during the post-boost phase because the rockets on the bus, being relatively small, do not give off much infra-red radiation.

The mid-course phase

In this phase of the flight the warheads and decoys travel together in a group through space. A modern ICBM, like the Soviet SS-18 and American MX, may carry a large group of up to 10 warheads and more than a hundred decoys, in addition to chaff and other means of fooling ballistic missile defences. While in the vacuum of space, all the objects in the group fly together along ballistic trajectories, irrespective of weight. Very light objects travel along precisely the same paths and at the same speeds as very heavy ones. No matter how precisely one tracks the objects in the cloud, it is virtually impossible to tell warheads from decoys. Therefore one would either have to shoot at all the warheads and decoys, or probe each object by some means to sort out the real warheads from the decoys before attacking the warheads. One way to distinguish between warheads and decoys in space is to scan each object with a laser beam. When the laser hits one of the group it will recoil, but a warhead, being much heavier, will recoil less than a decoy. This difference, it is said, could be used to distinguish between real warheads and decoys.

The Soviet ICBM force could produce a huge swarm of objects in space, containing perhaps as many as one hundred thousand targets for an American ballistic missile defence system to overcome. This statistic alone indicates the magnitude of the problem inherent in the Star Wars concept. It also brings home the importance of the defence destroying as many enemy missiles as possible during the boost phase, and early in the post-boost phase. In the boost phase the missile presents a single target. Once the missile's bus is emptied the number of targets, and thus the magnitude of the defence task, will increase a thousandfold.

At the highest point in its trajectory a typical ICBM warhead reaches an altitude of about 1,200 kilometres (750 miles). After passing through this point, the warheads, decoys, and other debris (including the bus) start to fall back to Earth, gaining speed as they fall. After spending 20 to 25 minutes in the mid-course phase, the warheads and accompanying objects re-enter the Earth's atmosphere at an altitude of about 100 kilometres (60 miles), or a slant range to the target, of about 250 kilometres (155 miles).

The terminal phase

The terminal phase begins when the warheads and the other objects travelling with them re-enter the Earth's atmosphere. At this point ICBM warheads are moving very rapidly indeed – at a speed of about 7 kilometres (4 miles) a second. As they penetrate the atmosphere, friction with the air rapidly increases and the temperature of each object quickly rises. The warheads are shrouded in their specially-shaped re-entry vehicles designed to withstand great temperatures – so they can survive the passage through the atmosphere to their targets. But the decoys and other accompanying objects are not protected against great heat and so burn up in the Earth's atmosphere, just as meteors (shooting stars) do.

The fact that decoys burn up in the atmosphere while warheads survive makes it easy to distinguish between them and raises the prospect of attacking the warheads in the terminal phase. But the main problem is that the time allowed for ballistic missile defences to engage incoming enemy warheads, once in this phase, is very short. By the time the decoys have burnt up, the warheads are at an altitude of 50 kilometres (31 miles) or so. A warhead would then be travelling at a velocity of about 10,000 kilometres (6,250 miles) per hour, so the ballistic missile defences have no more than a minute to intercept the warheads before they hit their targets. Moreover, the warheads would generally approach the ground at an angle of about 20 degrees to the horizontal – an awkward trajectory for the defence system to cope with.

Star Wars Weapons

Because of the curvature of the Earth's surface, Soviet ICBM silos are not in a direct line from any point in the USA. Soviet missiles can be attacked during their boost phase only by weapon systems deployed in space. The main weapons being considered for Star Wars are the so-called 'beam' or 'directed-energy' weapons, including high-energy lasers, particle beams, kinetic-energy weapons and microwave weapons.

The fundamental physical principles of these technologies are well known, but the actual development and engineering phases are yet to be entered. Most of the technologies and subsequent schemes for integrating them into a ballistic missile defence system are drawing-board concepts only. No one knows which will work as practical weapon systems and how effective they will be against, for example, Soviet countermeasures.

Laser Weapons

Laser weapons use laser beams to transmit energy to damage or destroy an enemy missile or warhead. Laser beams are essentially beams of radiation, such as light. When you switch on an electric light bulb, the light streams out of the bulb in all directions, illuminating the whole room. But radiation from the instrument known as a 'laser' (which stands for Light Amplification by Stimulated Emission of Radiation) goes in only one direction.

A laser beam is composed of rays that are almost perfectly parallel. The beam moves at the speed of light, 300,000 kilometres (187,500 miles) a second – the fastest speed that can be attained. Speed is all-important for a weapon designed to attack a ballistic missile from a long distance, during the missile's very short boost phase. Projectiles, such as bursts of laser energy that move at the speed of light, are therefore ideal for this purpose.

An enormous amount of energy can be concentrated in a laser beam – enough to cut a hole through a steel block several centimetres thick. If a high-energy laser were to hit a ballistic missile or its warhead, it would cause enough damage to render it ineffective.

Several types of lasers are potential Star Wars weapons. They include chemical lasers, excimer lasers, free-electron lasers and X-ray lasers. The difference between each type is the wavelength of the radiation in the beam. The radiation travels as a wave having crests and troughs; the wavelength is the distance between two neighbouring crests, usually measured in units of millionths of a metre called microns.

Chemical lasers emit infra-red light, excimer lasers emit ultra-violet light, free-electron lasers emit visible light, and X-ray lasers concentrate beams of X-rays. Lasers that emit infra-red, visible and ultra-violet light are usually called 'optical' lasers. Infra-red light has a longer wavelength than visible light which in turn has a longer wavelength than ultra-violet light. Visible light has a wavelength of about half a micron. The infra-red light in a typical chemical laser beam has a wavelength of about 3 microns and the ultra-violet light in an excimer laser has a wavelength of about 0.3 microns. X-ray lasers have very much shorter wavelengths than optical lasers. The wavelength of a typical X-ray laser beam would be about one thousandth (0.001) of a micron.

Chemical lasers

In a chemical laser, energy is supplied to (the experts say 'pumped into') the molecules of a gas. The pumping energy is provided by a chemical reaction – hydrogen and fluorine atoms are mixed together and react to form molecules of hydrogen fluoride. These molecules are able to store energy and in a laser they are stimulated to give up all their energy at once, in a cascade. One molecule gives up all its energy; this stimulates neighbouring molecules to give up their energy which stimulates even more molecules to give up their energy, and so on. The cascade forms a powerful beam of infra-red light.

A laser beam has two special properties. Firstly, the light rays in the beam all have exactly the same wavelength because they are all produced from the same transitions from the same types of molecules. Secondly, whereas the light waves from an electric light bulb are emitted at random so that there is no relationship between the crests and troughs of one wave and those of any other, the light waves emerging from the hydrogen-fluoride molecules of a chemical laser emerge with all the crests and troughs aligned. A beam of this special sort of light (called 'coherent' light) can be very narrowly focussed over a long distance using one or more mirrors, and can be made to carry a lot of energy.

Used as a Star Wars weapon, a chemical laser beam would be concentrated on an enemy missile or its warhead in much the same way as the rays from the sun can be made to set fire to a piece of paper by focussing them with a magnifying glass. An infra-red beam composed of parallel rays would be produced in a hydrogen-fluoride laser, then narrowly focussed and aimed onto its target by an accurately-shaped and precisely-oriented mirror, or if necessary, a number of mirrors.

High-energy lasers can damage a ballistic missile by burning a hole in its outer layer, called its 'skin'. The heat from intense infra-red radiation is intended to damage the booster's skin to the point where it will weaken or rupture. The missile fuel will then vent through such defects, resulting in the missile's failure. The difficulty in all this is delivering enough energy to the missile to disable it.

One problem is that there is a limit, defined by the laws of nature, to the smallness of the area to be focussed on by a perfect laser and perfect mirrors. For example, the combination of a chemical laser using hydrogen fluoride and a perfect mirror with a diameter of 10 metres (33 feet) will produce a 'spot' with a diameter of 1.1 metres (44 inches), at a distance of 3,000 kilometres (1,875 miles). If the laser beam contains 25 megawatts of energy the spot would have to stay at the same position on the missile for several seconds for enough disabling energy to be delivered. The development of a 25-megawatt chemical laser will certainly take a long time; current plans are for a demonstration of a 2-megawatt laser by 1987. If the enemy uses a heat-shield on the missile or equips it with a device to make it spin, the amount of energy needed to disable it would have to be significantly increased.

A second problem with using chemical lasers for

Star Wars is the production of large, high-quality mirrors. If the mirror is not precisely the right shape, the spot formed will be larger and the laser energy deposited per unit area on the enemy missile will be less. Even very small imperfections (and we are talking here of irregularities in shape of fractions of a micron) will significantly reduce the effectiveness of a laser weapon. And to achieve such geometrical perfection when manufacturing a curved mirror with a diameter of 10 or 15 metres (33 or 50 feet) is a formidable task. But the problems may not end there. The mirror has to be launched into space and must be able, without suffering any damage, to reflect a laser beam intense enough to burn the skin of an enemy ICBM. To withstand such treatment the mirror would have to be very robust.

A chemical laser producing a beam energetic enough to be effective for Star Wars would also use up a lot of fuel. For example, a 25-megawatt hydrogen-fluoride laser of extremely high efficiency would use about a ton of hydrogen-fluoride fuel every 20 seconds. The Soviets currently have about 1,400 ICBMs deployed. Assuming that a 25-megawatt laser beam takes four seconds to destroy a missile, and this is an extremely optimistic assumption, the laser weapons required to shoot down the Soviet ICBMs would use a minimum of 300 tons of hydrogen fluoride.

There has been a diversity of arguments over the calculation of the number of laser weapons that would be required to attack the entire Soviet ICBM force from battle stations in space orbits, while the missiles are still in their boost phase. Theoretically, if a laser weapon has 150 seconds available to attack enemy missiles during their boost phase, assuming an average of three seconds to destroy one missile, each laser weapon could intercept 50 enemy ICBMs. Laser weapons in space would be best deployed on battle stations in low Earth orbits. Each battle station would complete its orbit around the Earth in about 90 minutes, and it would be in sight of Soviet ICBM silos for only part of the time. So there must be enough battle stations in space to make sure that those with the Soviet ICBM silos in view carry the number of laser weapons required to destroy all the Soviet ICBMs. It is generally reckoned that it would take a total of roughly 100 orbiting chemical-laser battle stations to stand a chance of intercepting the entire 1,400-strong Soviet ICBM force. And the 100-strong fleet of battle stations would need to carry, at the very least, 2,000 tons of hydrogen fluoride to fuel the lasers.

Estimates like these are very approximate because of the crudeness of the assumptions made – a crudeness resulting from a lack of knowledge. To get the most optimistic forecasts one has to assume that lasers with very high performance can be developed, that optically-perfect focussing mirrors of very large size can be developed and built, that the mirrors can be turned from one target to another almost instantly, that the laser beams can be perfectly aimed, and that the decision concerning which laser fires at which booster takes up less than an instant. It will indeed be a long time before we know which of these assumptions are justified and to what extent.

It is also necessary to make assumptions about Soviet countermeasures. To what extent will the Soviets harden their ICBMs to reduce the damage done by an attacking laser beam? Will the Soviets deploy ICBMs with fast boosters to reduce the time that the laser weapons have to attack them? Will the Soviets attack the laser battle stations in space before launching their ICBMs? And so on. The answers to these questions will depend on the cost-effectiveness of ballistic missile defences, and we will not know this until we know more about the performance of the defence systems. The only calculations of the cost of space-based ballistic missile defences that can be done now are very rough back-of-the-envelope estimates.

Star Wars technologists have a long way to go before they can design and build a chemical laser powerful enough for use as a space-based weapon to destroy ballistic missiles during their boost phase. In the Office of Technology Assessment's publication *Directed Energy Missile Defense in Space*, Ashton B. Carter said: 'The current Alpha laser program of the Defense Advanced Research Projects Agency (DARPA) aims at a construction of a hydrogen-fluoride laser of just a few megawatts and built only for ground operation.' But he still claims that 'there is no fundamental technical reason why extremely bright chemical lasers cannot be built. In theory, several lasers can be operated together ... ten combined lasers would produce a beam 100 times brighter than each individual laser'.

Excimer and free-electron lasers
Another ballistic missile defence concept involves deploying excimer or free-electron lasers on the ground and putting mirrors in space. The laser beams would be aimed at the mirrors, which would reflect the beams back towards the Earth to attack Soviet ICBMs in their boost phase.

The word 'excimer' is short for 'excited dimer'. A dimer is a molecule containing two atoms, and in a laser the dimers would usually consist of an atom of xenon or krypton plus an atom of chlorine or fluorine. As with the hydrogen-fluoride, laser energy is pumped into the excimer laser; laser light is emitted when the molecules release this energy. But the process is very inefficient because only a small fraction of the energy put into the dimers comes out as laser light. Consequently, excimer lasers powerful enough to be used as Star Wars weapons would be very bulky and heavy, and would consume large amounts of electricity. This is why it is proposed that they are based on the ground rather than in space.

Whereas excimer and chemical lasers depend on the reaction between two atoms, a free-electron laser depends on the conversion of the energy carried by a beam of electrons into laser radiation. In a free-electron laser, a beam of electrons is accelerated to a high velocity in a machine and then passed into a tube called a 'wiggler' that has magnets placed along it. The magnets make the electrons wiggle to and fro as they pass down the tube. As the electrons wiggle they change their velocity and, in doing so, give off some of their energy as light. The emission of light by one electron stimulates other electrons to emit light, producing a cascade in the normal laser fashion. By adjusting the spacing of the magnets and the velocity of the electrons, the wavelength of the laser light can be varied considerably although, in practice, free-electron lasers are most likely to be operated at visible wavelengths. Like excimer lasers, free-electron lasers powerful enough to attack ICBMs effectively in their boost phase would be so bulky and complex that they will probably be ground-based if they are ever used as Star Wars weapons.

Granted that excimer and free-electron lasers are still in their early stages, some scientists believe that free-electron lasers have great potential for further development because (in theory at least) they should be much more efficient than excimer lasers – which so far have had very small energy outputs. The wavelength of the ultra-violet light in an excimer laser beam using krypton fluoride, for example, is 0.25 microns – one-tenth of the wavelength of hydrogen-fluoride infra-red laser light. This shorter wavelength means that a mirror with a smaller diameter can be used to focus a spot of a given diameter. A mirror used with an excimer laser would, however, have to be even more precisely machined than one used with a chemical laser; minute mirror irregularities would seriously degrade the performance of a laser weapon operating with ultra-violet light.

A Star Wars ground-based excimer or free-electron laser system would have a number of lasers with their mirrors deployed on mountain tops in the USA, and a number of large mirrors in orbit reflecting the laser beams around the curvature of the earth onto another set of mirrors. This last set would focus the laser beams onto separate enemy missiles as they ascend in their boost phase.

Passing a laser beam through the atmosphere and keeping it focussed is a very difficult job. The main problem is that turbulence in the air (due to variations in the air's density, the effect that makes stars twinkle) distorts the beam so that the crests and troughs of the individual waves in the beam no longer coincide exactly and the beam that emerges is a disorganized one. When reflected in the mirror system, even with optically-perfect mirrors, the beam will produce a much larger spot than if the crests and troughs of the waves in the laser beam coincided exactly.

Because of these atmospheric effects, it is proposed that ground-based lasers should be deployed on high mountains to try to reduce the length of the column of air through which the laser beam must pass. Even then, a ground-based laser system is only feasible if the effects of turbulence can be compensated for. George Keyworth, President Reagan's science advisor and an enthusiast for ground-based lasers, believes that the new technology of adaptive optics can be used to compensate for turbulence.

For use in Star Wars, the technique would consist of a low-power laser beacon positioned near the relay mirror in space orbit. A sensor on the ground would observe the distortion of the beacon beam as it passed through the atomosphere. The beam from the ground-based laser would then be predistorted in such a way that its passage through the same column of air, already passed through by the beacon beam, would modify it into an undistorted beam.

Adaptive optics technology, which has been used in a primitive way to improve the performance of some existing astronomical telescopes, is much more difficult than it sounds from this brief description and will take many years to develop to a point when it can be used for Star Wars applications. The mirror on the ground, for example, would have to be several tens of metres in diameter and made from tens of thousands of small elements, each individually adjustable, to give the required predistortion of the laser beam before it is reflected onto the mirror in space.

Ashton Carter describes a possible Star Wars laser configuration, using ground-based excimer or free-electron lasers deployed on mountain tops in the USA, in which four laser beams are used to attack 1,400 Soviet boosters launched simultaneously. The number four assumes that the laser beams can be instantaneously retargeted from one booster to the next. Any time delay in retargeting would increase the number of laser beams needed. Enough lasers are deployed so that at least four laser sites are always free of cloud cover. Ten relay mirrors would be positioned in space, each 30 metres (300 feet) in diameter. They would be launched into geostationary orbits, 36,000 kilometres (22,500 miles) above the Earth's surface.

One hundred intercept mirrors, each 5 metres (16 feet) in diameter and in low orbits, would be used to focus the laser beams onto Soviet boosters in rapid succession. These mirrors would be equipped with targeting devices to aim the laser beam accurately onto a booster; a possible targeting device could consist of a low-power laser and a telescope. The laser would illuminate the booster and the telescope would detect laser light reflected from the booster – and then aim the intercept mirror at it. All the mirrors must be even more precisely machined than for chemical lasers, and hardened to withstand the effects of heating by the laser beam.

Carter calculates that only about one-tenth of the energy of the laser beam leaving the laser would be focussed on a Soviet booster – the rest would be lost in the atmosphere and in reflection from the mirrors. This means that a very powerful laser indeed would be required. Carter suggests that each of the 12 lasers would need an output energy of at least 400 mega-watts, about the same output as that of a medium-sized electric-power station. In fact, given the huge amount of electric power that would be used by the lasers, and the remoteness of their mountain-top sites, specially designed power plants would probably be needed for them. The largest military laser now in operation has an output of only about 400,000 watts, so there is still a long way to go before the vast energy outputs needed are achieved.

X-ray lasers
American weapon laboratories, particularly the Lawrence Livermore National Laboratory, California, are enthusiastic about so-called X-ray lasers. Edward Teller, known as the 'father' of the H-bomb, believes that these devices have considerable potential as Star Wars weapons. In fact Teller is thought to have had great influence on President Reagan as he developed his Strategic Defense Initiative.

An X-ray laser uses a nuclear explosion to produce a directed beam of X-rays. It is sometimes called a 'third-generation' nuclear weapon, the first generation being the fission nuclear weapon (or atom bomb) and the second generation, the fusion nuclear weapon (or hydrogen bomb). An X-ray laser directs much of the energy of the nuclear explosion towards the target instead of emitting it in all directions like an ordinary nuclear explosion. The energy received by the target is, therefore, much greater than that of a hydrogen bomb of the same yield as the nuclear explosion used to pump the X-ray laser. The X-ray laser is therefore much more efficent than a second-generation nuclear weapon, just as a second-generation weapon is much more efficient than a first-generation nuclear weapon.

A significant amount of the energy produced by a nuclear explosion is released as X-rays. Some of these X-rays are pumped into a suitable lasing material to produce laser radiation at X-ray wavelengths. The wavelengths would be about one thousandth of a micron – very much shorter than the wavelength of visible light.

X-rays cannot be reflected by mirrors like the radiation from visible and infra-red lasers, so optical systems cannot be used to focus the X-rays into beams. But if the lasing material is in the form of a bundle of long parallel thin metallic fibres, the X-ray laser radiation will be emitted in beams.

The advocates of X-ray lasers as Star Wars weapons argue that the laser beams emerging from the rods could be used to attack enemy missiles. The nuclear explosion would, of course, quickly destroy the rods so that the energy from an X-ray laser weapon would come in one short intense pulse rather than in a continuous beam as from chemical, excimer and free-electron lasers. When the pulse of X-rays hit the enemy missile they would be rapidly absorbed by a very thin layer of the missile's skin, vaporizing it. This action would send a shock wave through the missile, shattering it completely.

The use of X-ray lasers as Star Wars weapons also poses problems. The X-rays of the wavelengths of the laser beams are rapidly absorbed by matter and cannot therefore penetrate far into the Earth's atmosphere. Consequently, an X-ray laser weapon would be unable to attack an enemy missile booster until it had risen to an altitude greater than about 80 kilometres (50 miles). Very little of the X-radiation would penetrate below this altitude. This constraint severely limits the use of X-ray laser weapons to attack missiles in their boost phase. And if the Soviets instigate an obvious countermeasure and reduce the boost-phase time by using powerful fast-burn boosters that burn out before reaching an altitude of 100 kilometres (60 miles) – then X-ray laser weapons would be useless for boost-phase attack.

X-ray lasers are potentially far less bulky than optical lasers, and because of their relatively low weight and volume, it is proposed that they should be launched into space only when American early-warning satellites signal that Soviet ICBMs have been launched (a concept known as the 'pop-up' system). Pop-up is favoured because the X-ray lasers would be much less vulnerable to an enemy attack than if they were deployed in space, although the laser weapons would still depend on space-based sensors. Also, because X-ray laser weapons are initiated by nuclear explosion, stationing them in space orbits is illegal under the 1967 Outer Space Treaty, which specifically prohibits the placing of any objects carrying nuclear weapons in orbit around the Earth.

Geographical considerations and the short time available to attack Soviet ICBMs in their boost phase eliminate the possibility of stationing X-ray laser weapons on the US continent, or even in Western Europe. The laser weapons would have to be boosted so high, and in such a short time to rise high enough to have a direct line of sight to the enemy missile before the booster burnt out, that a rocket of enormous power would be required. Basing X-ray laser weapons at any practicable location on land would require a rocket many thousands of times larger than the Apollo spacecraft that carried the US astronauts to the Moon, to hoist the X-ray laser into position.

Because operational X-ray laser weapons would be ineffective if located on land, it is proposed that they should be popped up from submarines, using fast-burn missiles. X-ray laser advocates argue that one laser weapon equipped with many lasing rods could attack perhaps a hundred or more enemy boosters. It is also said that if the weapons were launched from submarines close to the Soviet shores there would be enough time for the laser weapons to attack the enemy boosters. This may work on existing Soviet ICBMs – and if the whole process of warning the submarines, and launching and controlling the laser weapons, is fully computerized and virtually instantaneous. But if it took time to communicate with the submarines to instruct them to launch the X-ray laser weapons, or if any time was needed for human participation in the decision to launch, or if the Soviets replaced existing ICBMs with fast-burner missiles, submarine-launched X-ray lasers would be useless for attacking enemy ICBMs during their boost phase.

There are other problems associated with launching Star Wars weapons from submarines. Submerged submarines can only fire one missile at a time, with a time delay between each missile. The first missile firing may well be observed by an enemy reconnaissance satellite, which could pinpoint the position of the submarine. It could then be attacked and sunk before it had time to fire a second missile – especially when patrolling near to Soviet shores.

Even if the pulse of X-rays reached the missile in the boost phase, the enemy could protect his missiles from damage. X-rays of short wavelengths are rapidly absorbed by matter, actually making it easy to protect missiles from damage. For example, the skin of the missile could be made from two layers of metal. Garwin has suggested a design for a booster shield consisting of a metallic foil less than a millimetre thick and initially rolled up on a rod like a window shade. The device would be carried along the side of the booster as it rose up through the atmosphere. At an altitude of about 80 kilometres (50 miles), the rod would be pushed out from the booster and the foil unfurled to form the shield, which would absorb pulses of X-rays.

All in all, X-ray lasers are of very limited use as Star Wars weapons; if they are to be used at all for this purpose, it will be to attack enemy warheads *after* the boost phase. Yet in spite of their limitations the development of X-ray laser weapons is being energetically pursued in the USA – where they bear the code name Excalibur – and probably also in the USSR. A number of tests of nuclear-pumped X-ray lasers have already been made at America's underground nuclear test site below the Nevada desert. No information has been released about the results of the tests, although a March 1985 test which demonstrated the feasibility of X-ray laser weapons was described as a great success. However, in November 1985 reports in the Los Angeles *Times* by Robert Scheer, and in the magazine *Science*, claimed that scientists had found that measuring instruments were malfunctioning during the tests. But these setbacks seem not to have affected the funding of the X-ray laser programme.

The X-ray laser is seen by many as an exotic and glamorous technology, often used by SDI advocates to popularize Star Wars. It is also a contradictory aspect, considering the many statements by President Reagan that he opposes the use of nuclear weapons in his Strategic Defense Initiative, which he has frequently described as 'non-nuclear'.

Microwave-beam Weapons

Microwave radiation is yet another part of the electromagnetic spectrum – in addition to ultra-violet waves, visible light, infra-red waves and X-rays – being considered for use in a Star Wars weapon. Microwaves are radio waves of short wavelength (20 centimetres (8 inches) or so) used in radar, ground communications, and for cooking! The attraction of a microwave beam is that it is virtually unaffected by the atmosphere, so it could reach enemy missiles during the boost phase. But, after travelling only 200 kilometres (125 miles), even a very high-powered microwave beam would be so spread out that only a very small amount of energy per square centimetre would be deposited on the target – certainly not enough to damage the missile itself. However, even weak microwaves have dramatic effects on sensitive electronics and may be able to upset the missile's guidance system enough to stop it functioning. The main problem is that the microwaves would be absorbed by the skin of the missile and would only reach the electronics through apertures such as aerials, or through gaps in the skin. Taking all this into account, it looks like being a very chancy weapon indeed, and if used at all, would be as a secondary weapon.

Particle-beam Weapons

Particle-beam weapons, like lasers, would be designed to damage their targets by directing energy at them in a beam. But while laser energy consists of waves of electromagnetic radiation, particle beams are streams of atomic matter – usually charged particles (like protons or electrons), or neutral particles (like neutrons or atoms).

Charged-particle beams would not be suitable for Star Wars because although charged particles can be accelerated to produce high-energy beams, they would be uncontrollably bent by the Earth's magnetic field. A neutral-particle beam would not suffer from this disadvantage even though it has others. One such problem is envisaged when a neutral-particle beam passes through even the thinnest part of the Earth's atmosphere; here the neutral particles acquire charges, and the beam becomes unstable and uncontrollable as the charged particles spiral off under the effects of the Earth's magnetic field. This means that neutral-particle beams would have to be based in space; such weapons would be no good against missiles until the ICBMs had completely left the atmosphere and reached an altitude of about 160 kilometres (100 miles).

Existing Soviet ICBMs (such as the SS-18s) finish their boost phase at an altitude of about 400 kilometres (250 miles), but the Soviets could easily build ICBMs in the future with much shorter boost phases, intended to be over well before the missiles reach an altitude of 160 kilometres (100 miles). It is also doubtful whether neutral-particle beams will be really effective in damaging enemy missiles. Certain advocates suggest that neutral-particle beams could be used to damage the electronics in the missile's guidance system, others suggest that the neutral particles could be used to detonate the conventional high explosive in the warhead or even its nuclear material. But the precise nature and extent of such damage is not now known.

A neutral-particle beam weapon may use, for example, a beam of hydrogen atoms. This would be produced in a machine called an accelerator similar to those currently used in physics laboratories to produce beams of particles, in the study of atomic and sub-atomic matter. A neutral hydrogen atom beam would be produced by first adding electrons to ordinary neutral hydrogen atoms (which consist of one proton plus one electron) to give negative hydrogen atoms (consisting of one proton and two electrons). The negative hydrogen atoms are then accelerated in the electric field of the accelerating machine. As the beam leaves the accelerator the extra electrons are removed, leaving a beam of neutral hydrogen atoms. Because the effects of a neutral-particle beam on a missile are not known in any detail, it can only be predicted that a beam containing a very large number of high-energy particles (in other words, a beam of both high current and high energy) would be necessary to make an effective weapon. The next vital question is: can an accelerator powerful enough to produce such a beam, plus the power supply of many megawatts that would be required to run it, be produced in a size and weight suitable for launching them into space orbit? Once again, the technical problems involved are immense.

Kinetic-energy Weapons

Kinetic energy is the energy produced by a moving mass of material. As a kinetic-energy weapon, a projectile would use this energy to destroy a target. The greater the mass of the projectile and the higher its velocity, the greater is its kinetic energy. Some projectiles may also carry chemical explosives that explode on impact with the target.

The main problem here is not so much getting enough energy to the enemy missile to destroy it, but being able to make the projectile travel fast enough to reach the missile during the boost phase. Ashton Carter has analysed a number of scenarios using rocket-propelled kinetic-energy projectiles for effective boost-phase attack: 'a rocket-propelled kinetic energy system acting against today's Soviet ICBM arsenal (with no Soviet countermeasures) would require many heavy satellites and would be a dubious investment for the US'. Each satellite would have to carry a large number of kinetic-energy weapons. And again, if the Soviets deployed ICBMs with more powerful boosters to reduce the time of the boost phase, the US kinetic-energy weapon system would become useless and the Americans would either have to abandon it or invest huge sums in new satellites.

Despite this, kinetic-energy weapons are still being actively considered for attacking Soviet missiles in the post-boost and mid-course phases of their flight paths. A favourite candidate is not a rocket-propelled system but an ingenious device called an electromagnetic rail gun, which converts electrical energy to projectile kinetic energy.

In one proposed design, a rail gun consists of two parallel rails, the projectile being loaded between them. The rails and the projectile form an electric circuit through which a large electric current is passed. The current flow sets up a powerful magnetic field that propels the projectile forward. The projectile would be given such a high acceleration that when it left the gun it would be travelling extremely fast. This technique has been researched for a number of years. In 1978 an experiment was described in which small cubes were accelerated to velocities of 6 kilometres (3¾ miles) per second. A projectile weighing about 3 grams (0.10 oz) travelling at this velocity would be able to penetrate through several millimetres of steel – in fact this is similar to the system used by the Japanese to propel their high-speed 'bullet' trains.

Using an electromagnetic rail gun as a Star Wars

weapon would require a large electric-power source to operate it. Since the rail gun would have to be stationed in space, power would probably have to be provided by a nuclear-power reactor. The projectiles would also have to be made from special materials to withstand the effects of very high accelerations. And they would have to be steerable and provided with sensors to give terminal guidance, to enable them to home in onto the target – because of this, the projectiles are sometimes called 'smart rocks'! Given the very high relative velocity between the projectile and the target enemy warhead, ensuring an accurate interception will be difficult.

Back-up

These Star Wars weapons would be supported by a very complex array of systems based in space, on surface ships, in aircraft and on land. Very large relay mirrors to reflect beams from ground-based lasers would be stationed in geostationary orbits. Large numbers of mirrors would be in low orbits to focus laser beams onto enemy missiles rising in the atmosphere. Many satellites would carry radar and low-power lasers to distinguish between enemy warheads and decoys travelling through space. Other space-based radars, carrying huge aerials, would track warheads.

These space assets would have to be protected against attack. For this purpose, satellites carrying a large number of small missiles, fitted with infra-red and other sensors, would have to be parked near vital satellites, space-based weapons and other crucial orbiting systems to guard them.

Large numbers of radars and infra-red sensors, for surveillance and tracking warheads in their mid-course and terminal phases, would be carried by surface ships and aircraft operating globally. These systems would back-up very large, complex radars operating at sites around the perimeter of the USA and on the territory of its allies. Vast computers in a ground-control centre would manage the Star Wars battle; the time available in the early stages would be so short that humans would be excluded from making the decisions. Information for these computers would be continuously provided by the surveillance and tracking radars and infra-red sensors, and the fleet of early-warning, surveillance and communication satellites.

The Star Wars battle scenario is so complex as to almost defy the imagination. It is this sheer complexity, and the lack of any opportunity to test the systems under operational conditions, that cause the critics to doubt that Star Wars will work – even in the absence of Soviet countermeasures.

Other Threats

It should also be borne in mind that all the elaborate plans for ballistic missile defence make up just *one part* of a total strategic defence. Other areas include defence against strategic bombers; air-, ground- and sea-launched cruise missiles; anti-satellite warfare; anti-submarine warfare; civil defence of populations. The strategic ballistic missile threat is only a fraction of the total Soviet threat to the USA.

Submarine-launched Ballistic Missiles

A significant part of both Soviet and American strategic nuclear forces comprises submarine-launched ballistic missiles (SLBMs). The flight paths of SLBMs follow the same shape as those of ICBMs, but there is an important difference between the two. The exact location of the silos containing enemy ICBMs can be established from reconnaissance satellite photographs; the location of the other side's strategic nuclear submarines, carrying SLBMs, is not known.

Strategic nuclear submarines remain on station for long periods – typically about 70 days – keeping the targets of their SLBMs within range. The maximum range of a modern Soviet SLBM (like the SS-N-20) is about 8,300 kilometres (5,200 miles); that of a modern American SLBM (like the Trident C-4) is about 7,400 kilometres (4,600 miles). This gives the submarines a huge volume of ocean to lurk in.

If a submarine chooses to fire its missiles when it is close to its targets – that is, when it is near the enemy's shores – the flight time of the SLBMs will be very much shorter than that of ICBMs. SLBMs may have flight times of less than eight minutes compared with the 25 to 30 minutes taken by ICBMs. Moreover, if the submarine fires its missiles when on station close to the targets, the maximum altitudes of the missiles' trajectories will be much lower ('depressed trajectories') than those of missiles fired over longer ranges.

A possible scenario has SLBMs launched from unknown points from which they travel along depressed trajectories, reaching their targets relatively quickly. For these reasons, it is even more difficult for ballistic missile defences to deal with a large-scale attack by SLBMs than with an attack by ICBMs. Even when SLBMs fly in a normal trajectory over their maximum range, flight times are still significantly shorter than those of ICBMs. The boost and post-boost phases each last for less than three minutes; the mid-course phase, no more than 10 minutes; the terminal phase, less than one minute.

Modern SLBMs carry MIRVs. An American Trident C-4, for example, carries up to eight MIRVs and the Soviet SS-N-20, up to nine MIRVs, with each also carrying a large number of decoys. With such a short time in the mid-course phase, it would be extremely difficult to destroy all the warheads and decoys released by the bus, or to sort out which are the warheads and attack them. When faced with SLBMs in normal trajectories, ballistic missile defences would therefore have to concentrate on the boost, post-boost and terminal phases. If the SLBMs are flying in depressed trajectories the only realistic possibility would be to intercept the warheads during the terminal phase.

When SLBMs are fired over relatively short ranges, of less than, say, 3,000 kilometres (1,875 miles), the warheads re-enter the Earth's atmosphere at about half the re-entry speed of an ICBM warhead fired over its normal range. This makes them easier to intercept in the terminal phase than ICBMs.

Cruise Missiles

Ballistic missiles are not the only type of missiles in the strategic nuclear arsenals of the two superpowers. Both have also deployed cruise missiles – presenting a challenge to missile defences even greater than that presented by ICBMs and SLBMs.

A cruise missile is a small pilotless aircraft. It does not follow a ballistic trajectory but flies like an aircraft, using the aerodynamic principles of lift and drag. Modern cruise missiles (descendants of the German V-1 'buzz-bomb' used in the Second World War) are powered by small, very efficient turbofan or turbojet engines. Using the most efficient fuels, a cruise missile can carry a nuclear warhead over distances of several thousand kilometres.

Modern cruise missiles fly at subsonic speeds, at about 900 kilometres (550 miles) per hour – roughly the same as the cruising speed of a commercial airliner. But they are not as vulnerable as their slow speeds imply. Cruise missiles fly very close to the ground to avoid being detected by ground-based radars and shot down by surface-to-air missiles; by the time the radars have detected and identified the missiles, they will have flown past before a surface-to-air missile can be fired at them.

A cruise missile is able to hug the ground because of its sophisticated guidance system. The missile carries a computer into which is fed a flight plan to take the missile from its launch point to its target. An on-board radar set measures the altitude of the ground over which the missile is flying and compares it with a map stored in the computer's memory. Any divergence from the flight plan stored in the missile's computer is detected, and the course of the missile corrected, to bring it back onto the correct flight path. In this way the missile can be guided around hostile areas – those containing enemy air defences, for example – and taken to its target with great accuracy.

Cruise missiles can be launched from vehicles on the ground, or from aircraft, surface ships and submarines. If fired from a submarine, the launch position of the cruise missile cannot be predicted by the other side. Submarine-launched cruise missiles are, therefore, the most difficult to monitor using, for example, early-warning satellites.

The best defence against cruise missiles is to detect them from above, using aircraft called Airborne Warning and Control System (AWACS) aircraft, equipped with 'look-down' radar (this can detect objects in the air space beneath the aircraft carrying the radar). Fighter aircraft would be alerted and directed by AWACS to shoot down any enemy cruise missiles detected.

Because cruise missiles are unmanned and relatively cheap, an attacker would be prepared to accept relatively high losses. But future generations of cruise missiles are likely to be less vulnerable than today's versions. They will be designed to fly at much faster speeds – well above the speed of sound – making them much harder to detect. And they will also incorporate so-called Stealth techniques, in which aircraft are coated with radar-absorbing paints and are constructed in geometric shapes that make them less visible to radar.

A total missile defence would have to cope with attacks by large numbers of ground-, air- and sea-launched cruise missiles, as well as the onslaught of ICBMs and SLBMs. And one should not forget that American and Soviet strategic nuclear forces still have long-range strategic bombers carrying free-fall nuclear bombs as well as cruise missiles. Future strategic bombers will fly by computer so that they can penetrate enemy air defences by flying over them at very high speeds, but at low altitudes. Bombers will also use Stealth technologies to make them even harder to detect by radar.

In summary, cruise missiles and bombers could evade even the most effective ballistic missile defence system of the type envisaged in Reagan's SDI. If the USA is to defend itself against a Soviet strategic nuclear attack (and vice versa) it must have an effective air-defence system against bombers and cruise missiles, as well as effective ballistic missile defences. The deployment of such an air defence system alone would be an exceedingly costly undertaking.

Chapter 3

For and Against the
Strategic Defense Initiative

President Reagan's Stategic Defense Initiative ex-
presses an idea; it is not in any way an attempt to
describe a technological system. The faith behind the
idea is that if scientists and technologists are given
enough resources and encouragement they can solve
any problem. In the President's mind, the aim is to
design a system that will effectively defend the USA
against an all-out nuclear attack by the USSR. Such a
total defence would have to cope with ballistic
missiles, cruise missiles and bombers. No one
disputes that if it could be done, and nuclear
weapons made obsolete as a result, it would be a very
desirable thing only dreamed of so far.

The SDI quickly evolved into a research programme
set up to see if it is technologically feasible to tackle
one part of the total nuclear defence task – to defend
the US against a Soviet ballistic missile attack. No
one disputes the magnitude of the problem of
designing a ballistic missile defence, including the
scientists most responsible for organizing research
into the technologies. Thus, Gerold Yonas, chief
scientist of the Strategic Defense Initiative Organization, readily admits that 'it is quite clear that we have
a long way to go before achieving a thoroughly
reliable defense against ballistic missiles' because
the 'underlying issues and technologies . . . are far
from being fully resolved'. And Richard De Lauer,
who was the Pentagon's Under-Secretary for Research and Development, aptly remarked that to

develop the technologies for a ballistic missile defence would require several vast programmes, each the size of the Manhattan Project (the World War II A-bomb research programme) – each dealing with a different area of technology.

Some American scientists are keen to accept the challenge of Star Wars and believe that the technologies for an effective strategic nuclear defence will be developed. Not very surprisingly, many of these enthusiasts are working in the weapons industry or in weapons laboratories. George Keyworth, President Reagan's Science Advisor, is a typical representative of the views of such supporters in the scientific community: 'We can now project the technology – even though it hasn't been developed yet – to develop a defense system that could drastically reduce the threat of attack by nuclear weapons, not only today, but those that could reasonably be expected to be developed to counter such a system.'

The attitude from informed weapons experts is usually, however, one of cautious optimism about the prospects of solving this enormous technological challenge. This is well illustrated by the views of the experts commissioned to study the concept shortly after President Reagan made his Star Wars speech on 23 March 1983. The President ordered an extensive study into the feasibility of defending the United States and its allies from ballistic missile attack, and a research programme to be worked out for the technologies that could do this. Two separate blue-ribbon groups took part in the study, one headed by James C. Fletcher, formerly the administrator of the National Aeronautics and Space Administration, and the other headed by Fred S. Hoffman, director of a policy analysis organization called Pan Heuristics.

The two groups, made up mainly of aerospace experts from industry, weapons laboratories, research institutes and the Pentagon, worked between June and November 1983. Their results were integrated by an interagency group which recommended that $27,000 million should be spent on a research programme between Fiscal Year 1985 and Fiscal Year 1989 (inclusive), to investigate the technical feasibility of intercepting enemy ballistic missiles. A 50-strong team took part in the Fletcher study, called the 'Defensive Technologies Study'. Their conclusions were published in a report in March 1984.

The Fletcher team confined itself to defences against ballistic missiles and did not consider defences against cruise missiles or strategic bombers. The study reviewed, evaluated and placed priorities on the technological issues involved in the ballistic missile defence of the United States and its allies. It described a research and development programme 'to allow knowledgeable decisions on whether, several years from now, to begin an engineering validation phase that, in turn, could lead to an effective defensive capability in the 21st century'.

The team concluded that: 'The technological challenges of a strategic defense initiative are great but not insurmountable.' The report ends optimistically: 'The scientific community may indeed give the United States "the means of rendering" the ballistic missile threat "impotent and obsolete".' But even the most enthusiastic advocates agree that the time scale for the deployment of a full-scale ballistic missile defence system is long.

The sort of programme Star Wars optimists have in mind spans a period of about 30 years, from 1983 to about 2010, and is in four parts – a research phase, a systems development phase, a transition phase and a final deployment phase. The research programme, now under way, to examine the technical feasibility of missile defences is estimated to last until the late 1980s or early 1990s. If it were then decided to go ahead, the next phase would be the production of prototypes of ballistic missile defence systems and testing their components in space, when appropriate. Assuming this systems development phase went well, the third phase might begin in, say, the late 1990s. This would be a transition phase in which a start would be made on the deployment of the first increments of a ballistic missile defence system. The final phase, the deployment of a multi-layered defence system, might, according to the optimists, be completed around the end of the first decade of the 21st century. These time periods are, of necessity, very speculative; it must be remembered that no one knows which technologies will be developed for a ballistic missile defence, let alone when they will be developed – nor does anyone know the effectiveness of any such system that may evolve from these technologies.

The Arguments for Star Wars

The advocates for ballistic missile defence can be divided into four main groups. First, there are those who believe in the eventual possibility of a total defence against an all-out Soviet ballistic missile attack – the so-called 'astrodome' concept. This is seen as part of a grand attempt to make nuclear weapons 'obsolete'. This group, which includes President Reagan himself, apparently contains very few people who have actually made a detailed study of the issues involved. Most of the astrodome advocates have a rather blind faith in the power of technology to solve all problems. The group may not survive long after the Reagan Administration goes.

The second group of advocates are those who believe that, although a totally effective, leak-proof ballistic missile defence is probably not possible, a *near*-total defence may be attainable and, if it is, would be desirable. If, for example, a ballistic missile defence system was 90 per cent efficient in the boost and post-boost phases of the Soviet missiles' flight paths (taken together), 90 per cent efficient in the mid-course phase and 90 per cent efficient in the terminal phase, a dozen or so Soviet warheads would still get through to their targets. These warheads could cause great damage to the USA but, say those in the second group, the Soviets would be so uncertain about the effects of a nuclear strike that they would not make it in the first place. A nuclear attack would, they say, only be made if there was a probability that a large fraction of the warheads would reach the targets they were fired at. A near-total defence would, according to this argument, 'strengthen deterrence'. And if deterrence failed and there was a nuclear war, the defences would save millions of American lives.

The third group of ballistic missile defence advocates are those who believe in deploying ballistic missile defences not to protect cities, but to defend military targets, such as ICBM silos and military command and control centres. Such defences would, it is argued, improve the survivability of American retaliatory nuclear forces and hence strengthen deterrence.

The fourth group believe in having some ballistic missile defences which need not be comprehensive enough to be very effective against an all-out Soviet attack, but sufficient to deal with those Soviet nuclear forces that survive a pre-emptive American attack. These defences would be an essential element of a nuclear first-strike capability, and should therefore be deployed – so that the USA could reap the great strategic offensive advantage that a nuclear first-strike capability is said to bring. This group is small, and represents rather an extreme view.

It should be emphasized that this does not mean that there are many Americans in responsible positions who actually want to make a nuclear attack against the Soviet Union. But some do appear to want the international political advantages they believe a nuclear strategic superiority would give. And some believe that this is necessary to prevent the Soviets from eventually gaining a similar advantage which, they fear, might make them 'more expansionist'.

Of these four groups, the views of the first and the last are incompatible. One cannot argue that ballistic missile defences should be deployed to make nuclear missiles ineffective, so that they can then be eliminated, and, at the same time, argue that ballistic missile defences should be deployed as part of a policy of strategic nuclear superiority.

But the views of the second and third groups are compatible. One can argue that ballistic missile defences should be first deployed around military targets and that, if and when more exotic technologies are developed, these defences should be extended to cover cities – even though population defence will probably never be leak-proof. There are perhaps more advocates for this combination than for any other position, although it must be emphasized that there are many who argue for the deployment of ballistic missile defences around military targets, particularly ICBM silos, but are against their deployment for the protection of people. They support their case on the grounds that, because American ICBMs are vulnerable to a sudden attack, the American nuclear deterrent is weakened. And, they say, whereas the defence of ICBMs is justified to strengthen deterrence and is a move that would improve the stability of the Soviet-American strategic balance, the defence of cities would on the other hand be destabilizing – because it would limit the effectiveness of Soviet retaliatory nuclear forces, and thereby weaken Soviet nuclear deterrence.

Perhaps the case for the 'defence of military targets first, cities later' position has been best, and most thoroughly, put by Colin S. Gray, a leading strategist and President of the National Institute for Public Policy in Fairfax, Virginia. Gray bases his arguments on two main pillars. First, that nuclear deterrence based on mutual assured destruction cannot last for ever and that we must plan for a new nuclear policy. Secondly, that negotiations about nuclear disarmament between the USA and the USSR will only succeed once nuclear weapons have become ineffective. Only then, he says, will it be possible to negotiate them away.

Specifically, Gray says that American strategy has been dominated for decades by 'the offensive concept of deterrence': that is, by nuclear deterrence based on mutual assured destruction. This policy rests on the argument that neither the United States nor the Soviet Union will attack the other if it knows that its industry and population will be decimated in retaliation.

Gray believes that no offensive deterrent will work for ever and that its failure would lead to a nuclear world war, a consequence that he admits 'would be intolerable for civilization'. American vulnerability to Soviet nuclear weapons is not, he says, acceptable in the long term; the US has a duty to try to find a way to remove the threat of nuclear missiles. Moreover, the US government has a moral obligation to do what it can to save American lives. Gray believes that ballistic missile defence could, if the United States were ever attacked by nuclear weapons, save possibly tens of millions of American lives (and those of its allies) and 'kill no Russians in the process'.

To support his view that the deployment of effective

ballistic missile defences is the only practicable way to achieve nuclear disarmament, Gray points out that despite great efforts made since the Second World War by the USA and the USSR in bilateral negotiations, and by the international community in multilateral negotiations, they have all failed totally to secure nuclear disarmament. No nuclear weapons have been destroyed as a result of any treaty.

Gray argues that no nuclear disarmament has taken place because both sides believe that nuclear weapons have considerable political and military value, so until these weapons are seen to be totally useless, neither side will be willing to get rid of them. On the contrary, each side will continually strive to improve the quality of its nuclear weapons in an effort to achieve nuclear superiority. Gray concludes, therefore, that the only route to nuclear disarmament is by the deployment of ballistic missile defences. Then, 'nuclear disarmament will be politically and strategically feasible for the first time, both because nuclear delivery systems will not "work" in the face of a complex architecture of layered defense – meaning that states will choose not to waste scarce resources on such obsolete systems – and because the risks of disarmament will either be removed or very substantially alleviated, given that strategic defenses would be able to negate the value of any nuclear weapons that had been stockpiled covertly'.

Gray also argues for ballistic missile defences on moral grounds, claiming that they offer 'a possible way out of the moral dilemma that saps and threatens the very legitimacy of Western security policy'. This dilemma is that Western governments have a political duty to protect their citizens and their political and social values, but they also have a moral duty 'to defend humane values'. To defend one's society by nuclear deterrence by mutual assured destruction means threatening to trigger a nuclear holocaust, and being prepared to carry out the threat. The defence of the West thus rests on the threat to perform, if attacked, the most inhumane act possible and also on the intention to carry out this threat. Gray argues that an effective strategic defence would 'enable the United States and its allies to defend their values against nuclear intimidation or even actual nuclear assault without, in the process, negating everything they stand for'.

These arguments described above are typical of those used by advocates to justify both total and near-total ballistic missile defences, although Gray himself appears to believe that a totally leak-proof system is unlikely to be developed. (In practice, of course, if the Americans deployed extensive ballistic missile defences the Soviets would have no way of testing their effectiveness nor, for that matter, would the USA.) But he does believe that, irrespective of Star Wars, a limited defence of US strategic nuclear forces, particularly silos containing ICBMs, strategic bomber bases and important command, control and communication centres, will be developed and should be deployed.

He goes on to stress that such a partial system is not inconsistent with a 'future exotic defense of cities'. In fact, he argues, the two systems would be very compatible and even essential for a stable transition from nuclear deterrence based on mutual assured destruction, to a nuclear policy based on strategic defence.

Gray admits that the transition period from a limited defence of strategic nuclear forces using ground-based anti-ballistic missile systems (intended for deployment 'late in this decade') to the deployment of a 'comprehensive defence incorporating additional layers of more advanced technology' (requiring two decades or longer) could be dangerous 'if precautions were not taken to ensure political and strategic stability during that period'.

Gray sees danger in the possibility that the Soviet Union will achieve an advantage over the USA in nuclear defences, given 'its existing extensive radar network and rapidly deployable ground-based ballistic missile defence'. Even a limited Soviet system, he argues, combined with existing 'Soviet offensive first-strike capabilities, extensive air defense and civil defense preparations', could be very destabilizing.

What worries Gray is that the Soviet Union will have an offensive capability to destroy a large proportion of America's ICBMs by making a sudden, pre-emptive attack against them with its ICBMs. The Soviets, with their ballistic missile defences already begun, could then limit the damage that the surviving American nuclear forces could do in retaliation.

This combination of Soviet offensive and defensive capabilities, Gray argues, might increase the incentive for the USSR to make a first strike, particularly during a period of tense international crisis. But, he goes on, the deployment by the USA of a ballistic missile defence to protect its retaliatory strategic nuclear forces would greatly reduce the danger of a Soviet first strike – because Soviet military planners would be so uncertain of the effectiveness of a pre-emptive attack against American military targets that they would not be prepared to make the attack in the first place. (The discouragement of a Soviet first strike is, as has been seen, also used as an argument to justify comprehensive but *not* leak-proof ballistic missile defences. Such defences are seen as valuable for this reason, even if they turned out to be much less effective than was first planned.)

There is some disagreement among the advocates of ballistic missile defence about the dangers of the transition period from a limited system to a comprehensive one. Those who only want a limited system to defend military targets argue that to go further would be unacceptably provocative to the Soviets, who may even decide to make a pre-emptive attack to prevent the Americans deploying a large-scale nuclear defence. They argue that there is no way of making the transition period acceptably safe.

Gray, among others, is obviously hoist by his own petard here, because he readily admits that a comprehensive Soviet ballistic missile defence – coupled with an offensive capability that could limit America's retaliatory nuclear capability – would be unacceptable to the USA. He should therefore admit that a similar American capability would be equally unacceptable to the Soviets! If the American authorities would interpret a Soviet ballistic missile defence system as an element of a first-strike capability, then they must expect the Soviets to interpret an American system in exactly the same way.

Another source of discord among SDI advocates is about Soviet technological capabilities and Soviet intentions to deploy ballistic missile defences. Gray seems grossly to overestimate these. It is more usually believed that the Soviets are considerably behind the Americans in the appropriate technologies, particularly sensor and computer technologies; in any case, the Americans would know in time if the Soviets were intending to expand their ballistic missile defence system to any great extent. The idea that America could be taken by surprise is not a very credible one.

In addition to these major arguments in favour of ballistic missile defences, Gray gives some secondary ones. One secondary role is the protection of the USA against the accidental launch of a missile. Such an accidental launch could easily have catastrophic consequences and might lead to a nuclear world war.

Another secondary role is the protection of the USA against attack by a country with a small nuclear arsenal. Worries about nuclear weapons eventually spreading to countries that do not have them at present have caused concern that one of these countries (including ones known already to have nuclear weapons) may attack a superpower any time in the future and trigger off a nuclear world war.

The Technological Case Against

A powerful group of American scientists has argued against President Reagan's Strategic Defense Initiative ever since he announced it in 1983. Four of the most persistent Star Wars critics have full access to American classified information on ballistic missile defence. They are Hans Bethe, Richard Garwin, Sydney Drell and Wolfgang Panofsky. Because of their special knowledge, obvious expertise in the field and widely recognized eminence (Bethe, for example, worked on the first atom bomb), the views of these four scientists carry special weight.

Many other eminent scientists have supported their criticisms. For example, a group of 54 Nobel Prize winners signed an appeal against Star Wars. Particularly critical have been groups of computer scientists, such as Computer Professionals for Social Responsibility. In fact, it is no exaggeration to say that the great bulk of scientists outside the industries working on, or hoping to work on Star Wars technologies (the weapons laboratories, the defence ministries, the militarily-oriented think tanks) are at the least very sceptical about a comprehensive strategic defence for protecting cities and populations against a massive nuclear attack ever becoming technically feasible.

Many scientists who oppose Star Wars are not

Plate 1 The first space shuttle Columbia, begins its six hour journey to the launch pad in 1982. Following the destruction of the space shuttle Challenger on 28th January 1986 it will be at least 12 months before shuttle flights are resumed. In the longer term, however, the Challenger disaster is unlikely to impede Star Wars significantly.

Plate 2 Little is known about Soviet space shuttle activities. US reconnaissance satellites have observed the construction of a long runway at Tyuratam; the Soviet space launch centre. It is generally believed that this will be used by the Soviet space shuttle. The picture shows an impression of the complex at Tyuratam.

Plate 3 The interest in ABM systems has accelerated plans to construct space battle stations whose military tasks will include the carrying of high-energy lasers and other ballistic missile weapons. Shown in this illustration is one of several space station configurations developed by NASA for consideration by the US Government.

Plate 4 The Tracking and Data Relay System will consist of two specialised satellites, like the one in the picture, in stationary orbit and a ground terminal located at White Sands, New Mexico. The system will relay data, commands, video and voice to and from spacecraft and the ground terminal. The system was launched into orbit by the Challenger space shuttle.

Plate 5 A major military use of space is for communications. This is a typical communications satellite in orbit. It has 6.6 square metres (71½ square feet) of silicon solar cells mounted on two panels which always point to the Sun. The solar cells produce enough power (740 watts) to charge the nickel-cadmium batteries carried by the satellite to operate its communications equipment. The satellite's orbiting weight is about 450 kilograms (1,000 pounds).

Plates 6 & 7 The Galosh anti-ballistic missile interceptor and the Pushkino phased-array radar associated with the Moscow ballistic missile defence system. New high-accelerated missiles are being added to the Moscow system.

Plate 8 Soviet SA-X-12 surface-to-air missiles designed to intercept enemy aircraft. It is said that the SA-X-12 could be modified to intercept tactical ballistic missiles.

Plate 9 The Soviets are constructing this large phased-array radar at Krasnoyarsk which the Americans allege violates the ABM Treaty because it is not located on the periphery of the Soviet Union and facing outwards. The Soviets claim that

Plate 10 The Soviet anti-satellite weapon which destroys enemy satellites with a multi-pellet blast. When the enemy satellite hits the pellets it is damaged enough to make it inoperable.

Plate 11   F-15 in flight, carrying an anti-satellite missile. The aircraft will release the missile at an altitude of over 21,000 metres (70,000 feet) so that it can travel into space and attack a target satellite. It is guided by on-board sensors close to an enemy satellite and the warhead released to destroy the enemy satellite.

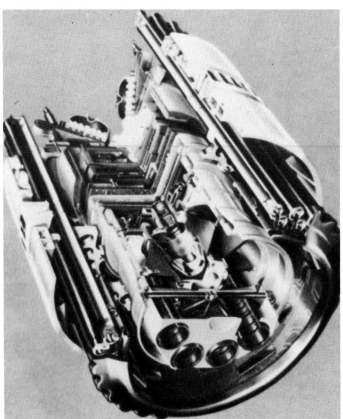

Plate 12   The homing head of the American anti-satellite missile. The US anti-satellite system could become fully operational in the second half of the 1980s.

Plate 13 Both superpowers are developing lasers for possible use in anti-satellite weapons. This artist's impression of a US laser anti-satellite weapon shows how a rotating mirror would be used to target the laser beam.

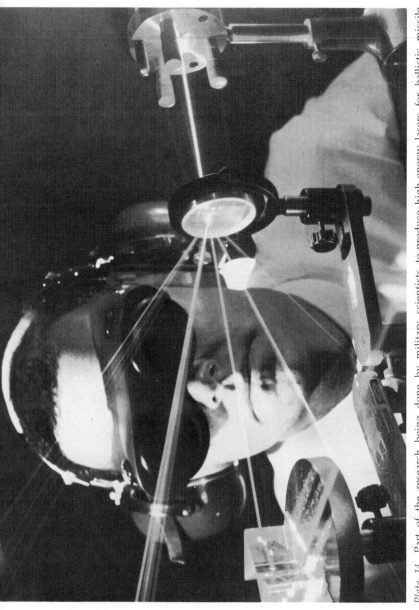

Plate 14 Part of the research being done by military scientists to produce high-energy lasers for ballistic missile defence and anti-satellite weapons.

Plate 15 Pictures of an aircraft being destroyed by a laser beam.

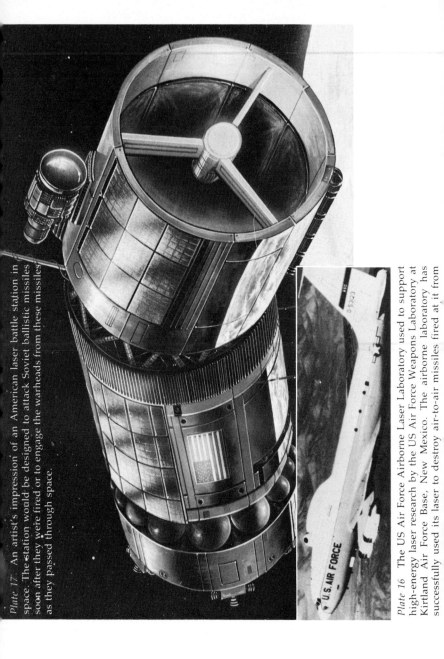

Plate 17 An artist's impression of an American laser battle station in space. The station would be designed to attack Soviet ballistic missiles soon after they were fired or to engage the warheads from these missiles as they passed through space.

Plate 16 The US Air Force Airborne Laser Laboratory used to support high-energy laser research by the US Air Force Weapons Laboratory at Kirtland Air Force Base, New Mexico. The airborne laboratory has successfully used its laser to destroy air-to-air missiles fired at it from

Plate 18 A particle-beam weapon of the type being considered for ballistic missile defence. The beam would either physically damage an enemy nuclear warhead in space or heat it enough to destroy it.

Plate 19 In a multi-layered ballistic missile defence system enemy warheads that survive the defensive weapons in space would be attacked by missiles fired at them from the ground. The US Army is developing non-nuclear warheads for ground-based anti-ballistic missiles. The programme is called the Homing Overlay Experiment, or HOE. The picture above shows a warhead. The metal ribs, about 2 metres (7 feet) long and seeded with steel weights, unfurl seconds before the HOE warhead collides with its target.

Plate 20 The anti-ballistic missile carrying HOE rises from its launch pad at the Kwajalein Missile Range.

against defence in principle, nor are they against a certain amount of research into ballistic missile defence systems. President Reagan's SDI is, after all, primarily a research programme to investigate the feasibility of new strategic defensive technologies, both Earth- and space-based. So why are scientists who are otherwise unopposed to research in general now objecting to the President's proposal, if it simply calls for research?

One main reason is that they believe that a research programme that costs tens of billions of dollars will lead willy-nilly to the deployment of some strategic defences, even if (as the critics judge will be the case) the research shows that only a partial ballistic missile defence is feasible. The deployment of anything short of an impermeable astrodome will, according to the critics, seriously destabilize the existing strategic balance between the USA and the USSR – and thereby undermine US national security. And, they point out, even the director of the SDI Office admits that an impermeable system 'is not on the cards'. In short, the Star Wars opposition argues that any strategic defence system short of the full protection of cities is unacceptably dangerous and that James Schlesinger, a former US Secretary of Defense, is right when he says: 'in our lifetime and that of our children, cities will be protected by forbearance of those on the other side, or through effective deterrence' but not by strategic defences.

A group of SDI opponents, including Richard Garwin and Hans Bethe, have published detailed criticisms in a book, *The Fallacy of Star Wars*, published by the Washington-based Union of Concerned Scientists. This, and the report *Ballistic Missile Defense Technologies*, produced by the US Congress's Office of Technology Assessment (OTA), are perhaps the most authoritative critiques of strategic defence.

The vulnerability of ballistic missile defences is highlighted by the fact that the adversary could frustrate the defences by deploying ICBMs with much more powerful engines than current models, so that the boosters would burn out rapidly while still in the Earth's atmosphere. A 50-second boost phase is feasible, ending when the missile is at an altitude of about 80 kilometres (50 miles). This would make it virtually impossible to attack the missiles during the boost phase. The enemy could also deploy decoy ICBMs – boosters without warheads – to saturate boost-phase interceptors.

Because the main aim of a comprehensive ballistic missile defence is to destroy missiles during their boost phase, and because geography determines that Soviet silos cannot be seen from United States territory, American ballistic missile defence weapons must attack Soviet missiles from space. So the defensive weapons will have to be deployed on orbiting space battle stations before the attack begins, or launched into space very rapidly after the early-warning satellites have detected the start of an ICBM attack.

According to *The Fallacy of Star Wars*, battle stations in space are extremely vulnerable to a large variety of attacks – in fact, much more vulnerable than the ICBMs they are designed to destroy. The likely countermeasures adopted by an adversary would give him the advantage of their being based on technologies that are already well understood; most of the exotic technologies for attacking missiles during the boost phase have yet to be developed. The position of battle stations in space would also be well known to the other side as they would stay in known orbits for a long time. So they could be effectively attacked by the likes of space mines – satellites containing explosives placed by the enemy in orbits near to the battle stations. The mines would be detonated by remote control by the enemy at exactly the same time as he fired his ICBMs.

Another way to destroy a space battle station is given in *The Fallacy of Star Wars*. An enemy satellite could be put into the same orbit as the space battle station, moving in the opposite direction and releasing objects to cripple it. 'A one-ounce steel pellet moving at 16 kilometres [10 miles] per second (the relative velocity between the space battle station and the enemy satellite) would penetrate 15 centimetres [6 inches] of steel. It is not possible to defend a ballistic missile defense battle station against such a simple and relatively cheap mode of attack'.

Also extremely vulnerable would be the huge mirrors deployed in space to reflect high-energy laser beams onto enemy ballistic missiles. As Garwin *et al.* point out: 'Few targets are more attractive than a 10-meter [33-foot] mirror that must retain its shape and reflectivity to a high degree of perfection to perform its task'. Only a fine cloud of dust released by an enemy satellite would be needed to damage the mirror's surface, making it incapable of focussing a laser beam adequately.

It would be very difficult to protect the mirror. Shields would be of little use against, for example, steel pellets travelling at 16 kilometres (10 miles) a second. To quote Garwin *et al.* again: 'one might try to have the mirror unassembled or folded up if there were no alert. But it is not easy to design a 10-meter [33-foot] mirror that can be pointed with precision better than one part per million toward a target, that must attain a shape accurate to better than a micron, and that can be unfurled as quickly as an umbrella.'

If the enemy would (as Star Wars critics argue) have little difficulty in deploying countermeasures to make sure that his missiles survive the boost phase, he would have less difficulty in making sure that most of his missiles avoid mid-course interception.

This is so despite the fact that the ballistic missile defence systems would have a much longer time to intercept ballistic missiles in the mid-course phase than in the boost phase. The attacker could frustrate the defence by releasing hundreds of decoys from each missile. Irrespective of their weight and shape, the decoys would follow exactly the same trajectories as the real warheads. By making it impossible to distinguish between decoys and warheads, the attacker can force the defence to intercept every object. A few hundred missiles could easily carry enough objects to overwhelm the defence.

Garwin *et al.* describe various types of decoys in *The Fallacy of Star Wars*. Some are subtle: for example, a balloon might be tied to a warhead, with a short distance between them. An interceptor, aimed at the composite target, may well pass between the decoy and warhead, missing both.

In addition to ordinary decoys, the attacker can use chaff (clouds of metallic strips) to saturate the radars used by the defence. To depress infra-red radiation, and confuse any infra-red sensors used by the defence, the attacker could have the two warheads covered with aluminized plastic, which could also be used for decoy balloons. This would considerably reduce the heat radiated by the warheads and decoys and confuse the defence's infra-red sensors. The attacker can also make his re-entry vehicles carrying the warheads less vulnerable to interception by high-energy lasers during the mid-course phase of the flight path, by rotating them – thus reducing the local heating effect of the laser beam.

During the terminal phase of a ballistic missile's flight, there are a number of ways to frustrate the defence – especially a comprehensive defence system tasked with the protection of the entire population. When the target is a city, the attacker could deliver warheads of very large explosive yields, which could be detonated at high enough altitudes to escape any terminal defences. For example, a warhead with an explosive yield equivalent to that of 20 million tons of TNT, exploded at a height of 30 kilometres (19 miles) would destroy a large city by fire and blast. The Soviets have made warheads with this enormous yield. Another device to frustrate terminal defences is the manoeuvring warhead; this would be fitted with small wings to allow it to manoeuvre as it approached its target, further complicating the defence's task of plotting its flight path.

Major weaknesses in any strategic defence system are the radars and other sensors and the battle-management systems for tracking enemy missiles and warheads, also vital for command, control and communications. These would be large targets, some deployed on space battle stations, for the attacker to destroy fairly easily. The loss of even a small fraction of the tracking, command and control capability would destroy the comprehensiveness of a strategic defence.

Such detailed consideration of the technical problems facing the creators of ballistic missile defences lead Garwin *et al.* to conclude: 'The proliferation of warheads and decoys in midcourse, and the insoluble problems of protecting cities in the terminal phase of a strategic attack, conspire to place the burden of ballistic missile defense schemes on boost-phase interception. And this is a burden that the current schemes for ballistic missile defense cannot bear.'

Cost-effectiveness

No one really knows the cost of an effective comprehensive ballistic missile defence – because we simply do not know which combination of technologies, if any, will be suitable for the purpose. We do not know how strategic nuclear forces will evolve, and so we are ignorant of the nature of the offence. Nor do we know how future systems, such as high-energy lasers and particle beams, will perform. Given this ignorance, it is impossible to calculate essential parameters for a ballistic missile defence, such as the number of space battle stations that would be required.

Nevertheless, some cost calculations have been made, based on crude assumptions and guesses. There seems to be a growing consensus that roughly 100 space battle stations would be needed for a ballistic missile defence system to counter the current Soviet ICBM forces of 1,398 ICBMs, in the boost phase. At about $2,000 million per station (a reasonable figure) the bill for space battle stations alone would come to $200,000 million. These crude calculations are the basis for statements, such as those made by former Secretaries of Defense Harold Brown and James Schlesinger and by various Pentagon spokesmen, that a full-scale strategic defence would cost several hundred thousand million dollars – possibly as much as a million million dollars.

Some authors have estimated the cost of a limited ballistic missile defence system. Once again, these are based on simplistic assumptions and must be taken with a pinch of salt. Zbigniew Brzezinski, Robert Jastrow and Max Kampelman, for example, calculate that the cost of establishing a boost-phase defence system adequate for a limited defence would be roughly $45,000 million. This would supposedly pay for 100 satellites, each holding 150 interceptors, four geosynchronous satellites and 10 low-altitude satellites dedicated to surveillance and tracking, and centres for ground-control communications and battle management. They estimate the cost of a terminal layer of defence to be about $15,000 million, including $10,000 for 5,000 interceptors (heat-seeking missiles) and $5,000 million for 10 aircraft carrying instruments for tracking the Soviet warheads. This $60,000-million system would, of course, be a relatively unsophisticated, limited, two-layered system, designed simply to upset Soviet calculations about the possible success of a sudden attack on the USA and thereby to reduce the likelihood of such a Soviet first strike.

Paul Nitze, a veteran American arms control negotiator and now special advisor to the President and Secretary of State on arms control matters, has explained that an acceptable strategic defence must be 'survivable and cost-effective'. The Nitze criterion of cost-effectiveness (to be used to decide whether or not to deploy a strategic defence) relates to the marginal cost ratio, or the cost of the defence compared with the cost to the adversary of increasing the number of their strategic missiles needed to overcome the defence. There is a hot debate over this. Garwin *et al.* ask: 'What would be the cost trade-off if the Soviets were to deploy a cluster of 3,000 small three-warhead fast-burn ICBMs at a cost of about $50,000 million?' They calculate that to counter these additional missiles, nearly 1,000 space battle stations would be required at a cost of some $1 million million, a ratio of 20 to 1 *in favour of the offence*!

Robert Jastrow, former director of the Goddard Space Flight Center and a fervent advocate for Star Wars, argues that the Garwin *et al.* calculation is based on the assumption that the Soviets will develop an ICBM with a 50-second boost phase which, he says, is unrealistic. He assumes Soviet boosters which have a 180-second boost phase (similar to the US MX ICBM) and calculates that the number of space battle stations required to attack 3,000 such Soviet missiles goes down to about 100, which would cost about $100,000 million. He also estimates that it will cost the Soviets far more than $50,000 million to deploy the 3,000 missiles. In fact, he says, the cost is likely to exceed $400,000 million – giving a ratio of 4 to 1 in favour of the defence.

These two sets of calculations, giving entirely different results, demonstrate their *ad hoc* nature. The truth is that we just do not know enough to make meaningful statements about the cost-effectiveness of a strategic defence. What we can say for sure is that the absolute cost of deploying a comprehensive strategic defence would be enormous – certainly hundreds of millions of dollars.

The Destabilization Problem

The critics and advocates of President Reagan's Strategic Defense Initiative agree about one thing: that if a comprehensive defence able to protect the entire American population against an all-out Soviet nuclear attack could be *developed and deployed very rapidly*, it would be very desirable indeed. But, say the critics, not only is such an elaborate defence technically impossible, now and in all probability for ever, but even if it were not, it would most definitely take a very long time to develop and deploy. Even the keenest advocates admit that the deployment of a comprehensive strategic defence is 20 or 30 years away. Such a delay is crucial when considering the political and strategic consequences of Star Wars.

The critics of the SDI say that the instigation of a large, multi-billion-dollar research programme leading to the incremental deployment of a ballistic missile defence system will, in itself, inevitably have grave political and strategic consequences. This leads the critics to argue that, even if they are wrong about the technical problems and a comprehensive strategic defence could be built, it should still not be brought to fruition because relations between the superpowers would become extremely unstable in the period during its deployment. The probability that a nuclear world war would occur during this period of instability is too high to be acceptable.

The critics also believe that the Soviets will interpret American strategic defences as a component of an American nuclear first-strike capability. They will fear that the Americans will acquire the capability to destroy a large fraction of their strategic nuclear forces by making a surprise (pre-emptive) attack, then going on to destroy any surviving Soviet nuclear forces that hit back with their strategic defence system. The Soviets would, in other words, fear that a US ballistic missile defence would reduce their retaliatory, second-strike forces enough to rob them of their own credible nuclear deterrence based on mutual assured destruction.

Since the Soviets would almost certainly not be prepared to allow the Americans to gain such a strategic advantage, the deployment of a ballistic missile defence may well provoke them into making a nuclear attack on the USA before this deployment had gone so far as to give the Americans a strategic advantage. The Soviets would, as countries usually do when making military decisions, base their conclusions on worst case analysis. They would assume that American defences would work better than they actually would in practice – perceiving that their strategic nuclear forces would be under a greater threat than would in fact be the case. This could make the Soviet leaders panic, especially during a period of international crisis when relations with the USA were particularly tense, increasing the danger of a nuclear attack on the USA, however irrational such an attack might be.

Star Wars critics and advocates are diametrically

opposed over destabilization. Even though the various groups of advocates differ about some of the consequences of the deployment of ballistic missile defences, they all agree that even a partial defence would reduce the danger of the USSR making a nuclear first strike against the USA and would therefore decrease the danger of nuclear war between the USA and the USSR. This implies that the United States would, under no circumstances, contemplate making a nuclear first strike against the Soviet Union.

The critics of SDI, however, argue that it is unreasonable to expect the Soviets to have such faith in American good intentions, and that they would never allow a situation to develop where they perceive the USA to be in a position to make a nuclear first strike. Therefore the deployment of a partial ballistic missile system would, the critics argue, *increase* the danger of the nuclear war the ballistic missile defences are supposed to prevent.

Even President Reagan acknowledged the potential destabilizing consequences of the initiative. 'I clearly recognize that defensive systems have limitations and raise certain problems and ambiguities', he said in his March 1983 speech. 'If paired with offensive systems,' he went on, 'they can be viewed as fostering an aggressive policy, and no one wants that.'

As has been seen, some advocates of ballistic missile defences are, like the critics, worried about the destabilizing dangers of transition to a large-scale nuclear defence system and, for this reason, prefer to limit American defences to military targets. But other advocates get around this problem, by arguing that the mere threat of the deployment of ballistic missile defences will encourage the negotiation, fruitless so far, of reductions in the numbers of strategic nuclear weapons deployed by the USA and the USSR. In fact, it is often said by US officials that a reduction in strategic offensive forces is an essential counterpart to the deployment of strategic defences. The idea is that when ballistic missile defence systems are developed (but before they are deployed), the Americans will negotiate reductions in offensive nuclear weapons with the Soviets to maintain the strategic balance. This theory that strategic offensive weapons will necessarily be reduced as a result of setting up strategic defences is central to SDI. And it is essentially an admission that a strategic defence could be rendered ineffective if the adversary increased his offensive strategic forces.

But is the theory of SDI stimulating this reduction realistic? No, say the critics. The most obvious Soviet response to an American ballistic missile defence is to overwhelm it by deploying more missiles – particularly large ICBMs carrying more warheads and decoys than current models. Consequently, the Soviets will be unwilling to negotiate reductions in their offensive strategic weapons while the Americans continue to pour huge resources into SDI. This is particularly true if the Soviets interpret such defences as part of an American first-strike capability.

Star Wars advocates in favour of a large-scale deployment try to get around this difficulty by arguing that the Soviets will have an economic incentive to negotiate offensive nuclear weapon reductions. American Defense Secretary Caspar Weinberger, in a speech on 5 December 1985, said: 'Strategic defense offers the Soviets a real incentive for major arms reductions. They would have no reason to continue their huge investment in offensive arms. It is quite apparent that they would like some reason for discontinuing this so that they would be able to devote more of their resources to trying to improve their disastrous economic situation at home.' Weinberger emphasized that strategic defence 'is not another means of trying to gain an offensive advantage'.

In the final analysis, one's judgement about the desirability of Star Wars must depend on whether one believes that the Soviets will accept Weinberger's word that the USA has no aggressive nuclear intentions. This really is the crux of the matter. The fact that the Americans are continuing to develop and deploy nuclear weapons of types seen to be more useful for fighting a nuclear war than deterring one (*see* American Nuclear War-fighting Capability) while, at the same time, the President is preaching the virtues of strategic defence, is bound to raise the suspicion that the Americans are seeking strategic superiority.

American Nuclear War-fighting Capability

For all general intents and purposes the Soviet and American nuclear arsenals are so huge, with so much 'overkill' on each side, that a rough parity may be said to exist between them. But there are important specific differences. For example, the Soviets are able to keep at sea only about one in eight of their strategic nuclear submarines, whereas the Americans keep about two in three of their strategic nuclear submarines at sea at any one time. This means that a force of fewer than ten Soviet strategic nuclear submarines are at sea, compared with a force of more than 20 American ones.

The Soviet submarine fleet is also disadvantaged by geography. To get out into the Atlantic and Pacific Oceans, Soviet submarines must sail through three narrow channels: one from the north of Scotland to Iceland to the Arctic icecap, one north of Norway to the ice and one north of Japan. These channels are monitored by Western anti-submarine warfare sensors so that the Americans know when a Soviet submarine enters the two major oceans. The Americans, on the other hand, have free access to both the Atlantic and the Pacific and their submarines cannot be monitored by Soviet sensors.

Another source of asymmetry between their strategic nuclear arsenals is in the Soviet emphasis on ICBMs. About 70 per cent of Soviet strategic nuclear warheads are carried by ICBMs compared with about 20 per cent of the American warheads. Any increase in the vulnerability of their ICBMs would be of great concern to the Soviets.

Another disparity is technological. The Soviet Union is, in general, some years behind the US in military technology, indicated by the fact that Soviet strategic nuclear warheads are cruder and less accurate than their American counterparts. To be able to destroy specific targets they have at present to be of higher yield (they are – twice that of American warheads). Miniaturization leading to more sophisticated guidance systems and greater accuracy has enabled the Americans to develop smaller weapons equally destructive of military targets at longer range, and less costly.

The available public information about American nuclear-weapons stockpiles has been recently published in *The Nuclear Weapons Data Book* by the American weapons experts W.M. Arkin, T.B. Cochran and M.M. Hoenig. The Data Book shows that relatively few changes were made in American nuclear weapons during the 1970s, but that dramatic changes are planned for the 1980s and into the mid-1990s, involving the projected production of some 30,000 new warheads during that time. About 14,000 of these are weapons in current research and development programmes, with the likelihood that the US will deploy 23,000 or so new nuclear warheads during the 1980s. About 17,000 nuclear warheads will be withdrawn from the stockpile or replaced during this period. And so by 1990 the American nuclear stockpile will contain about 32,000 weapons. This number was reached only once before, in 1967.

From what little we know of Soviet plans, and from what we can surmise from the history of Soviet nuclear-weapon deployments (which have tended to follow those of the USA but with a time delay of a few years), we must expect the Soviets to increase their nuclear arsenal to the same extent as the Americans.

Huge and formidable though these increases in the numbers of nuclear weapons are, quantity is far less important than qualitative improvements. There is already so much 'overkill' in the nuclear arsenals that even large increases in numbers are strangely of little relevance to the nuclear policies of the superpowers – they simply make an irrational situation somewhat more irrational. Only a small number of nuclear warheads is in fact needed for a credible policy of nuclear deterrence based on mutual assured destruction (MAD). There are at most 200 cities in each superpower nation with populations greater than 100,000 people. Assuming two nuclear weapons are needed to destroy a large city, then about 400 warheads would be more than enough for an adequate nuclear deterrent – more than enough to kill roughly 100 million people and destroy half the industrial capacity in each superpower. These figures indicate the absurd amount of overkill in the nuclear arsenals. An adequate deterrent could be had with 400 or so nuclear warheads and yet each superpower has about 10,000 strategic nuclear weapons targeted on the other!

The most crucial advances in nuclear weapons are those which improve their accuracy and reliability.

Very accurate ballistic missiles can deliver nuclear warheads over intercontinental ranges on smaller targets than less accurate ones. This means that, as these weapons become more accurate, they are increasingly on military sites. Many of the new strategic nuclear weapons being deployed may therefore be deemed more suitable for fighting a nuclear war than deterring one by MAD.

The accuracy of a nuclear warhead is normally measured by its Circular Error Probability (CEP). This is defined as the radius of the circle centred on the target, within which a half of a large number of warheads of the same type fired at it would fall. Both the Americans and the Soviets are reducing the CEPs – thereby increasing the accuracy – of their nuclear-weapon systems, including their ICBMs, SLBMs, strategic cruise missiles, and tactical nuclear weapons.

The Americans have in particular improved the guidance systems of the Minuteman ICBM, specifically by improving the pre-launch calibration of the gyroscopes and accelerometers that guide the missile during the boost phase. These improvements have reduced the CEP from about 400 metres/440 yards (its value at the end of the 1970s) to about 200 metres/220 yards (its current value). At the same time, the design of the Minuteman warhead was improved so that for the same weight, volume, radar cross-section and aerodynamic characteristics, the explosive power of the warhead was increased from 170 to 330 kilotons.

It is interesting to compare the efficiency of the new Minuteman warhead with the Hiroshima bomb. The latter exploded with a power equivalent to that of about 12,000 tons of TNT, devastating the city; the bomb physically weighed 4 tons. The ratio of the explosive yield to weight (the measure of a munition's efficiency) was 3,000. The new Minuteman warhead has an explosive power equal to that of

330,000 tons of TNT and weighs about 300 kilograms (a third of a ton), giving a yield-to-weight ratio of more than 1 million. This vast increase in the efficiency of nuclear weapons, achieved in just over 30 years, is just one indication of the incredible rate at which military technology advances, (even though the difficulties of Star Wars may be beyond it).

The new higher-yield Minuteman warhead, delivered with this increased accuracy, is able to destroy a Soviet ICBM in its silo (hardened to withstand an over-pressure of about 675 kilograms/1,500 pounds per square inch) with a probability of success of about 60 per cent. If two warheads are fired at the Soviet silo the probability of destroying it is about 90 per cent.

The new American ICBM, the MX, will be even more accurate than the Minuteman. The guidance for the MX uses an all-altitude guidance system (called the advanced inertial reference sphere) that can correct errors of the missile's movements (often incurred during lift-off) before it is fired. A CEP of about 100 metres (110 yards), one-half of the CEP of the Minuteman, can be achieved with this system. The MX warheads may also be fitted with terminal guidance, in which a laser or radar set in the nose of the warhead scans the ground around the target as the warhead travels through the Earth's atmosphere towards the target. The laser or radar locks onto a distinctive, fixed feature in the area – such as a tall building or a hill – and guides the warhead with great accuracy onto its target. With terminal guidance, MX missiles will have CEPs of 30 metres (33 yards) or so.

The MX ICBM is huge; it has a launch weight of about 86,000 kilograms (85 tons), about more than twice the launch weight of the Minuteman. It can carry warheads weighing a total of 3,500 kilograms (3½ tons), enough for 10 MIRVs each with a yield of

330 kilotons The three MX booster rockets will use advanced solid propellants, very light motor cases and advanced nozzles to propel the missile twice as efficiently as the Minuteman. And the boost phase of the MX is 180 seconds – much shorter than that of the Minuteman. MX ICBMs will first be deployed in existing Minuteman silos at the end of 1986, but it is uncertain how many. The Reagan Administration requested 100 but in 1985 the US Congress agreed to fund only 50 MXs. The Americans are also developing a new small, mobile ICBM carrying a single warhead, to replace the MXs in the 1990s; it will be called Midgetman.

The most formidable Soviet ICBM is the SS-18. Its CEP is, or soon will be, about 250 metres (275 yards) and its warhead probably has an explosive yield of 500 kilotons. This warhead would have a 60 per cent probability of destroying an American ICBM in its silo; two warheads fired in succession would have about a 90 per cent chance of success. The USSR has 308 SS-18s in service, almost all of them carrying 10 MIRVed warheads each. The SS-18 ICBM force, 3,000-plus warheads strong, is therefore a significant threat to the American 1,000-missile-strong ICBM force. In theory, three SS-18 warheads could be targeted on each American ICBM.

The Soviet SS-19 ICBM was believed by American intelligence agencies to be as accurate as the SS-18, and with a similar warhead, as great a threat to American ICBMs. Each SS-19 may carry six MIRVed warheads so that the total force of 360 missiles would be able to deliver 2,160 warheads. But the CIA has recently revised its estimates, now claiming that the SS-19 is not accurate enough to be a serious threat to American ICBMs. There has, however, been no change in American Intelligence estimates of the accuracy of the SS-18, which is still seen to be a threat.

Because of the increasing vulnerability of land-based ICBMs, greater attention is being given to strategic nuclear submarines and the missiles they carry. Both superpowers are now busily modernizing their submarine fleets. The USA plans to deploy about one new Trident submarine a year for the next few years – at a cost of about $2,000 million per submarine. The US Navy envisages a fleet of some 25 Tridents early in the 21st century. Six are already operational, the seventh should become so in 1986, and the eighth is scheduled to begin sea trials in May 1986.

The first eight Tridents will be fitted with Trident C-4 (also called Trident-1) SLBMs. But the ninth Trident, currently due to become operational in 1988, will be equipped with the Trident-2 SLBM. The Trident-2 will have a longer range than the Trident-1, so the submarines carrying it will be able to operate in much larger areas of the oceans and still be in range of targets in the Soviet Union. The submarines will then be less exposed to Soviet anti-submarine warfare (ASW) systems. If the US Navy's plan to operate 25 Trident submarines early in the next century comes about, the submarines will carry 600 Trident-2 SLBMs equipped with 6,000 nuclear warheads – each with an explosive power of about 500 kilotons.

Trident-2 warheads will be very accurate. Whereas the CEPs of the Poseidon C-3 and the Trident-1 missiles are about 450 metres (500 yards), the CEP of the Trident-2 will be about 200 metres (220 yards). This improved accuracy will be achieved by mid-course guidance and more accurate navigation of the submarines. The use of terminal guidance will increase the accuracy even more; with it, CEPs can be expected to come down to roughly 50 metres (55 yards). Within a few years, then, American SLBMs will be as lethal as ICBMs.

114

The USSR is also improving the quality of its SLBM force, presently thought to be less accurate than their American counterparts. The CEP of the SS-N-18, for example, is probably about 600 metres (660 yards), although the SS-N-20 and the SS-NX-23, now under development, are almost certainly more accurate.

Fifty metres (55 yards) or so are the best CEPs attainable for ballistic missiles. Once this plateau is reached by the US, it will be only a matter of time – probably three to five years – before the USSR catches up.

Current American nuclear policy is a confusing mixture of MAD and nuclear war-fighting (also known as Nuclear Utility Targeting Strategy, or NUTS!). SLBMs provide the MAD element, being still inaccurate enough to be targeted on cities only, while ICBMs are now nuclear war-fighting weapons, accurate enough to be targeted on enemy strategic nuclear forces and other military targets. But when Trident-2 SLBMs are deployed in the late 1980s they will be accurate enough to be targeted on military targets in the USSR – American nuclear policy will completely go from MAD to NUTS.

If a large number of tactical nuclear war-fighting weapons, such as enhanced-radiation weapons (neutron bombs), are deployed as anti-tank weapons in Europe, they will be integrated into military tactics at low levels of command. Then, not only will a war in Europe almost inevitably escalate to a nuclear war, but the military will more easily come to believe that a nuclear war is 'fightable and winnable' and that a 'limited nuclear war' is possible. This belief in the fightability and winnability of nuclear war will make such a war more likely. And this is the danger of the deployment of strategic and tactical nuclear weapons seen to be useful mainly for fighting a nuclear war.

A range of military technologies is being developed that will strengthen this belief that a nuclear war can be fought and won. Two such believers, Colin Gray and Keith Payne, have argued that 'the United States should plan to defeat the Soviet Union and to do so at a cost that would not prohibit US recovery', and that 'a combination of counterforce offensive targeting [i.e. attacking military targets], civil defense, and ballistic missile and air defense should hold US casualties down to a level compatible with national survival and recovery.'

The most important of the 'war-winning' technologies now under development are for anti-submarine warfare (ASW), anti-ballistic missiles and anti-satellite warfare systems. The aim of strategic ASW is to detect and destroy, within a short time, all the enemy's strategic nuclear submarines within range of one's homeland. Great secrecy surrounds ASW developments. For example, the US Navy is working with blue-green lasers, possibly deployed on satellites, to detect submarines − but little is known about the results of this work. From time to time statements are made by US naval spokesmen implying an existing capability to detect and destroy Soviet strategic nuclear submarines, at least those close to the US coast, but we have few details about current strategic ASW capabilities. But even in the absence of a technological breakthrough − which may, of course, be made − we can be sure that steady progress will be made in limiting the damage that could be done by enemy SLBMs.

When one side can severely limit the damage inflicted by the other side's strategic nuclear forces in a retaliatory strike, and believes it can destroy any enemy warhead that survives a surprise attack by ballistic missile defences, then the temptation to make an all-out first strike may become well-nigh irresistible, particularly during an international crisis. And it is the potential use of ballistic missile defences as a component of such a first strike that Star Wars critics worry about most.

Star Wars and Arms Control: the Existing Treaties

The testing and deployment of weapons and components for ballistic missile defence will have serious consequences for arms control. Existing treaties will be affected and so will the prospects for negotiating new treaties.

If a ballistic missile defence weapon system such as an X-ray laser used a nuclear explosion in the atmosphere or in space, two treaties would be violated. The 1963 Partial Test Ban Treaty prohibits the carrying out of a nuclear explosion 'in the atmosphere, beyond its limits, including outer space'. And then there is the 1967 Outer Space Treaty itself. This bans the placing in orbit around the Earth of any objects carrying nuclear weapons, the installation of such weapons on celestial bodies, or the stationing of them in outer space in any other manner. The USA and the USSR are not only parties to both treaties, but were the main instigators of them.

The treaty mainly put at risk by new developments in ballistic missile defences is the 1972 US-Soviet ABM Treaty, which limits the deployment of anti-ballistic missile systems – the term used for ballistic missile defences in those days.

The ABM Treaty prohibits the deployment of ABM systems for the defence of the *whole territory of the USA and the USSR*, allowing the deployment of ABMs around two areas only in each country – one for the defence of each capital, the other for the defence of one ICBM complex each. No more than

100 anti-ballistic missiles and 100 launchers for anti-ballistic missiles may be deployed in each of the two permitted areas. The ABM Treaty also limits the number of radars that can be deployed 'for an ABM role', and subjects these radars to qualitative restrictions. In the deployment area, defined in the treaty as a circle with a radius of 150 kilometres (94 miles) and centred on the national capital, there can be 'ABM radars within no more than six ABM radar complexes, the area of each complex being circular and having a diameter of no more than three kilometres [1.8 miles]'. Around an ICBM site (also defined as a circle of 150-kilometre/94-mile radius), the treaty allows the deployment of 'two large phased-array ABM radars comparable in potential to corresponding ABM radars operational or under construction on the date of signature of the treaty' and no more than 18 ABM radars, each of a potential less than the smallest of the two phased-array radars. The treaty prohibits the future deployment of radars for early warning of strategic missile attack except at locations along the periphery of the USA and the USSR, and facing outward.

A phased-array radar uses a fixed flat area consisting of many small aerials for transmitting and receiving signals, instead of the familiar single mechanical rotating aerial. Each signal is redirected from target to target electronically in a very short time. A phased-array radar can rapidly gather information about a large number of targets in a short time, a job that would require a large number of traditional radars using mechanically-steered dishes. Phased-array radars are crucial for ABM systems because of the need to pick up and track a very large number of targets almost simultaneously.

The ABM Treaty bans the development, testing or deployment of ABM systems or components that are sea-, air-, space-, or mobile land-based. Also banned is the deployment of ABM systems using technologies other than interceptor missiles and radars. Subject to these and the other treaty provisions, the modernization and replacement of permitted ABM systems or their components may be carried out. Most important in the context of the Star Wars programme is the fact that the treaty does not prohibit research into new ABM systems or components; *research* into new ABM technologies is allowed, but their *deployment* is not.

On 25 May 1976 a Protocol to the ABM Treaty came into force, limiting ABM deployment to one area rather than two. Each party had to choose whether this should be the national capital or an ICBM site. Because the USA favoured the Safeguard silo-defence ABM system, it opted for the deployment of ABMs around an ICBM site rather than around Washington. An ABM system, consisting of Perimeter Acquisition Radar, a Missile Site Radar and silos for Sprint and Spartan anti-ballistic missiles, was constructed around the Minuteman ICBM wing at the Grand Forks US Air Force Base, North Dakota. This ABM installation was declared operational on 1 October 1975, just three years after the ABM Treaty. The very next day, Congress ordered the Safeguard system dismantled. Since then, American ballistic missile defence activities have been limited to research.

When the ABM Treaty came into force, the USSR had begun to deploy an ABM system around Moscow. It decided to retain this system which, after the US dismantled its ABMs, became the world's only operating ABM complex. The Soviets have continually modernized the Moscow ABM system and, like the Americans, have continued research into new ballistic missile defence technologies.

This seemingly clear situation established by the treaty is somewhat clouded by an Agreed Statement

(D) between the USA and the USSR, attached to the treaty. This says: 'the parties agree that in the event that ABM systems based on other physical principles and including components capable of substituting for ABM interceptor missiles, ABM launchers, or ABM radars are created in the future, specific limitations on such systems and their components would be subject to dicussion in accordance with Article XIII and agreement in accordance with Article XIV of the treaty'. The Soviet–American discussion about new ABM systems would take place in the Standing Consultative Commission set up under the treaty (Article XIII). Each party can propose amendments to the treaty, and every five years 'the parties shall together conduct a review' of the treaty to see that it is working satisfactorily (Article XIV). Agreed Statement D recognizes that new technologies would come along, and tries to deal with them in the spirit of the treaty.

Until recently, it was assumed that the US Government, like virtually everyone else, believed that permission to develop and test 'ABM systems based on other physical principles' applies *only to fixed land-based systems*. As recently as April 1985, in the Arms Control Impact Statement made by President Reagan to the US Congress, the White House made it clear that it interpreted the treaty in this way. In other words, the Reagan Administration up to this time had accepted that the ABM Treaty banned the development, testing and deployment of space-based weapons. Moreover, American officials made it clear that President Reagan's SDI would be pursued in a way that was consistent with the generally accepted interpretation of the ABM Treaty. So everyone was taken by surprise when, on 6 October 1985, President Reagan's National Security Advisor Robert McFarlane said on American television that the White House had changed its mind about the ABM Treaty – and now interpreted it as allowing the development of space-based ballistic missile defence systems and the testing of these systems, including testing in space.

Under this interpretation, confirmed by McFarlane in a press conference on 8 October, the only thing prohibited by the treaty is the deployment of such systems. The justification given for this dramatic change in interpretation was based on the ambiguities in the record of the ABM Treaty negotiations – a claim that cannot be checked because such records are kept secret. The new American position seems to be that the development and testing of ABM systems that involve 'new physical principles' are 'approved and authorized by the treaty'.

The McFarlane statement was, not very surprisingly, heavily criticized by many Americans and by America's allies, and of course, by Soviet spokesmen. The US Arms Control Association, for example, talked of 'Reagan's new ABM Treaty', saying: 'The Reagan Administration has adopted a new version of the Anti-Ballistic Missile Treaty – a version which will permit the United States and the Soviet Union to engage in much more extensive work on space-based defenses than would have been permitted under the earlier version as it was universally recognized from 1972 to 1985. In fact, the new version will allow any development and testing activities short of final deployment of a full space-defense system.' The Arms Control Association goes on to point out that 'it seems most unusual for an administration that claims the United States is a decade behind in strategic missile defense, to favor a new version of the ABM Treaty that will free the Soviet Union to make much greater efforts to hold or even increase the alleged lead. But this outcome, according to one US official, is a "realistic" view of our new treaty revision.'

121

Despite this, the Administration is sticking to its position and regards the new version as the legally binding one. Secretary of State George Shultz, in an attempt to calm down NATO Governments who were astounded that the US should drop such a bombshell just before the Reagan–Gorbachev Geneva Summit, hastened to explain that, although the new interpretation was perfectly valid, the US would, for the time being, behave according to the previously-accepted, more restrictive interpretation of the ABM Treaty! In a speech to a North Atlantic Assembly meeting in San Francisco on 14 October 1985, Shultz said: 'It is our view, based on a careful analysis of the treaty text and negotiating record, that a broader interpretation of our authority is fully justified. This is, however, a moot point; our Strategic Defense Initiative research program has been structured and will continue to be conducted in accordance with a restrictive interpretation of the treaty's obligations.'

US officials have not said how long the US will continue to act according to the original interpretation of the treaty, but one must assume that it will start testing components of a space-based ballistic missile defence system when it is ready to do so. Presumably, the Soviets would follow suit and the ABM Treaty would be a dead letter – at least in so far as its original intention, which was to stop the testing, development and deployment of a *nationwide* ballistic missile defence system, is concerned. There is great irony in this situation. When US Secretary of State George Shultz met Soviet Foreign Minister Andrei Gromyko in Geneva on 7 and 8 January 1985, they solemnly agreed to reverse 'the erosion' of the ABM Treaty!

If the purpose of the ABM Treaty is to be preserved – and remember that many experts are convinced that the failure of this treaty will rapidly lead to strategic instability – activities on ballistic missile defence must stop at the end of the research stage. But what does this mean in practice? The former US negotiator, Ambassador Gerard Smith, explained:

> The prohibition of development contained in the ABM Treaty would start at that part of the development process where field testing is initiated on either a prototype or bread-board model . . . The fact that early stages of the development process, such as laboratory testing, would pose problems of verification by national means is an important consideration in reaching this definition. Exchanges with the Soviet delegation made clear that this definition is also the Soviet interpretation of the term 'development'.

Given Ambassador Smith's experience in the negotiations, his statements can be taken as definitive. It is true that they were made in 1972 – but nothing has changed since then except, of course, the US Administration.

Some American experts do not think that the ABM Treaty should be preserved. In fact, some openly argue that the US should withdraw from it. Colin Gray, for example, says: 'The United States certainly has sound strategic and arms control reasons to reconsider its continued endorsement of the ABM Treaty. At the time the treaty was signed, the United States established a clear linkage between offensive and defensive arms control limitations. Such a linkage made good sense; the United States could accept severe limitations on ballistic missile defences, which might defend US ICBMs and strategic bomber bases, if the Soviet offensive threat to US retaliatory forces could be constrained and reduced on a long-term basis through arms control.' Thus US Unilateral Statement A, accompanying the ABM Treaty, stated specifically that 'failure to achieve agreement within five years, providing for more comprehensive limitations on offensive forces than those contained in SALT I, could be grounds for withdrawal from the ABM Treaty'.

Because, according to Gray, this requirement has not been met, the Americans 'have a strategic and arms control rationale' and a legal right to withdraw from the treaty. But Gray does not argue for such a revision, or withdrawal from the treaty to happen immediately. He believes that the progress of the US ballistic missile defence programme will in any case not be far enough advanced for the ABM Treaty to be affected at least before the late 1980s. When the testing and development process begins to violate the ABM Treaty, though, he would have no hesitation in initially revising and then withdrawing from it.

To summarize, if Star Wars stays within the research stage the ABM Treaty is unaffected. The Reagan Administration has already modified the Treaty unilaterally to allow the development and testing of any space-based ballistic missile defences, but has said that, for the time being, the Strategic Defense Initiative will go ahead within the original 'restrictive interpretation' of the treaty. The current status of the ABM Treaty is therefore uncertain – but it seems that the Americans could decide, as soon as they want to test a component of a ballistic missile defence system, to go over to their 'new version of the Treaty'. This is, to say the least, an odd way for a superpower to conduct its international affairs.

Star Wars advocates argue that in practice the ABM Treaty will not impede the US programme for a few years, but that as soon as the programme enters the testing and development phase the US should first seek revisions to the treaty and then withdraw from it.

Prospects for Arms Control

The supporters of a treaty limiting anti-satellite weapons became particularly anxious when President Reagan's Administration showed no intention of resuming the Soviet–American bilateral talks on limiting anti-satellite weapons started by President Carter. In July 1982 President Reagan announced his decision that the Pentagon should go ahead with the development and testing of the F-15 anti-satellite weapon, and that it was his intention 'to deny any adversary the use of space-based systems that provide support to hostile military forces'. This seemed to signal a wish that the Americans should achieve a dominant military position in space.

In response to this policy of increasing military strength but decreasing efforts to achieve some arms control, some leading American experts presented a draft anti-satellite weapon treaty to the US Senate Foreign Relations Committee in May 1983. This activity was organized by the Washington-based Union of Concerned Scientists which has played, for many years, a major role in the debate in the USA about the military use of space. The success of the Union's lobbying efforts is shown by the way the US Congress has cut since 1983 the Administration's requests for funding anti-satellite weapon programmes, also voting for a moratorium on testing the F-15 system.

The draft treaty has three crucial elements:

—The signatories (i.e. the USA and the USSR) would undertake not to destroy, damage, render inoperable or change the flight trajectories of space objects.
—The signatories would undertake not to test in space or against space objects weapons for destroying, damaging, rendering inoperable, or changing the flight trajectories of space objects.

125

Furthermore, the signatories would undertake not to place such weapons in orbit or to station them on celestial bodies or in outer space in any other manner.
—Compliance would be verified by national technical means, enhanced by cooperative measures and buttressed by collateral constraints on other space activities to prevent circumvention of the treaty's provisions.

The Union of Concerned Scientists' treaty is a modest proposal and is not a fully comprehensive ban on anti-satellite weapons. President Carter's negotiators, for example, tried in 1978 and 1979 to get a more comprehensive treaty, also prohibiting any possession of anti-satellite weapons and requiring existing ones to be dismantled or destroyed. The Union is pressing for a limited ban because a more comprehensive ban would be far more difficult to verify. And this would give ammunition to those who will always use any conceivable difficulties about verification as a major argument to oppose a treaty. The Union has stated:

The major difficulty in a ban on possession would probably come from the US F-15 anti-satellite weapon, which is small. Intrusive on-site inspection would be required to verify that it is not deployed unless the Soviet Union were to be satisfied that they could acquire this knowledge by other means. While the large size of the Soviet anti-satellite weapon would make the dismantling of the launchers used in past tests readily observable, it is not clear whether other launchers used in the Soviet space program could substitute for this purpose.

Some NATO Governments are concerned about the anti-satellite warfare activities of the two superpowers. The British Foreign Secretary, Sir Geoffrey

Howe, said in a surprisingly forthright speech on 15 March 1985:

> We must recognize the heavy Western dependence upon the existing utilization of space technology and particularly upon satellites for intelligence purposes. We must also recognize that the prospect, at a time of crisis, of either side being faced with the loss of its strategic eyes and ears would be gravely destabilizing. It could provoke a new and even more threatening stage in any East–West confrontation.
>
> In the case of anti-satellite systems, the future is now. The Soviet Union has already deployed such a system at low altitude, and the United States is in the middle of a successful testing programme. By contrast, any development beyond the research stage of defences against ballistic missiles (the most immediate nuclear threat) is many, many years away.
>
> The Government takes the view that if negotiations were to succeed in imposing mutual constraints on anti-satellite systems, these could have a helpful impact over a period of years. We should take that opportunity now, if it is in the Western interest. Any such anti-satellite agreement could be limited to a fixed period, in order not to prejudge the future.

In August 1983 the USSR submitted to the United Nations a multilateral draft treaty on the prohibition of the 'Use of force in outer space and from outer space against Earth'. Under the treaty the signatories would undertake not to test or create new weapons systems, to destroy existing ones and not to deploy any space-based weapons. This draft treaty has been submitted to the Conference on Disarmament in Geneva but it has not been possible so far to set up a working group to negotiate such a treaty.

There is little hope of progress in negotiations for a treaty banning or limiting anti-satellite weapons unless the US Government really wants it. At the moment it does not. The White House believes that the US needs anti-satellite weapons to counter 'the threat that Soviet reconnaissance satellites present to US military forces'. In any case, it argues that 'adequate' verification of such a treaty would not be possible – that the Soviets may cheat and suddenly deploy anti-satellite weapons they had secretly developed.

Cynics may feel now that the US will not even discuss any limitation on anti-satellite warfare activities with the Soviets because they do not want in any way to hinder or constrain the future US development, testing and deployment of ballistic missile defences. But the main arms control negotiations now going on between the US and the USSR are the Nuclear and Space Weapon talks in Geneva. These were initiated when US Secretary of Defense George Shultz and Soviet Foreign Minister Andrei Gromyko met in Geneva on 7 and 8 January 1985. The negotiations cover three areas – strategic nuclear arms, intermediate-range nuclear forces (intermediate-range missiles like the SS-20, Pershing-II and ground-launched cruise missiles deployed in Europe up to the Urals) and space weapons (whether the latter are based on Earth or in space). The two sides agreed to try to negotiate treaties that would 'end the arms race on Earth, and prevent one in space; limit and reduce nuclear weapons and strengthen strategic stability'. Following the November 1985 Summit President Reagan and General-Secretary Gorbachev agreed in a joint statement to accelerate the Nuclear and Space Weapon talks.

President Reagan announced on 10 June 1985 that the USA would continue to observe the provisions of the 1979 SALT II Agreement. The Soviets have announced that they too will obey the provisions. SALT II, never ratified by the US Senate, expired on 31 December 1985; this treaty has in effect limited US and Soviet strategic nuclear forces since 1979. According to the US Arms Control Association, if the SALT II limits are abandoned before a new agreement on strategic nuclear forces is reached, by 1990 'the Soviet Union could increase its total number of nuclear warheads and bomber weapons by almost 7,000, roughly twice the increase that the United States could make over the same period, and 4,000 more than the Soviets could deploy without SALT II'. This illustrates the importance of both sides sticking to the SALT provisions and the advantage to the US if they do so.

During the 1985 Nuclear and Space Weapon talks at Geneva both sides tabled a bewildering series of proposals, counter-proposals and counter-counter-proposals. As of the beginning of 1986, the US position was:

On strategic offensive forces

1. Reductions to a limit of 4,500 on warheads on ICBMs and SLBMs.
2. Reductions to a limit of 3,000 on warheads carried by ICBMs.
3. A 50 per cent reduction in the highest overall strategic ballistic missile throw-weight of either side – that is, from the Soviet level of 5.4 million kilograms (53,147 tons) (the US has 2 million kilograms/1,968 tons). (The throw-weight of a missile is its payload.)
4. A limit of 1,500 on the number of long-range air-launched cruise missiles carried by US and Soviet heavy bombers.
5. Reductions in strategic ballistic missiles, ICBMs and SLBMs, to a limit of 1,250 to 1,450.
6. A limit of 350 on heavy bombers.

7. A ban on all new heavy strategic ballistic missiles and the modernization of existing heavy missiles.
8. A ban on all mobile ICBMs.

On intermediate-range nuclear forces
1. A limit of 140 Pershing-II missiles and ground-launched cruise missiles (the number deployed on 31 December 1985).
2. A limit on the Soviet SS-20 missile launchers within range of NATO Europe of 140. The Soviets to reduce SS-20 launchers in Asia, outside the range of NATO Europe, by the same proportion as the reductions of SS-20 launchers within range of NATO Europe.

On space weapons
1. The US states that 'it remains committed to the Strategic Defense Initiative research program as permitted by, and in compliance with, the 1972 ABM Treaty'.
2. The US proposes that the USSR joins in 'an open laboratories' arrangement under which 'both sides would provide information on each other's strategic defense research program, and provide facilities for visiting associated research facilities and laboratories'.

The major Soviet proposals on strategic nuclear forces at the beginning of 1986 were not very different to those put forward by the US. Each side should be limited to 6,000 nuclear 'charges'. By the Soviet definition, 'nuclear charges' includes gravity bombs and short-range nuclear missiles carried by bombers. Of the 6,000, not more than 60 per cent can be in any one category – land-, sea- or air-based. The USSR would thus be allowed a maximum of 3,600 ICBM warheads and the Americans 3,600 SLBM warheads. There should be a freeze on the deployment of cruise missiles with a range of more than 600 kilometres (375 miles). No limit on strategic-missile payloads is proposed by the Soviets.

On intermediate-range nuclear forces, the Soviets propose a limit of 120 American cruise missiles in Europe and no Pershing-IIs. Soviet warheads aimed at Europe would be cut to this number, plus a number equivalent to the number of warheads on British and French strategic nuclear forces.

On space weapons, the Soviets propose that activities on ballistic missile defences not covered by the 1972 ABM Treaty should not go beyond laboratory research.

On 15 January 1986 Gorbachev took many people in the West by surprise by proposing a timetable for complete nuclear disarmament, going far beyond the proposals then tabled at Geneva. The Gorbachev plan would eliminate nuclear weapons by the year 2000 in three stages, reminiscent of the General and Complete Disarmament Treaties proposed by the USA, the USSR and the UK in the early 1960s. Both superpower political leaders have now proposed the elimination of nuclear weapons – Reagan by Star Wars and Gorbachev by treaty.

The first stage of the Gorbachev plan, to be completed 'within the next five to eight years', includes the elimination of Soviet and American intermediate-range forces (ballistic and cruise missiles) from Europe. During this stage, the USA and the USSR would also agree to halve their strategic nuclear forces, that is, negotiate the sort of reductions in strategic nuclear weapons already proposed by the Soviets and Americans. Each side would agree to retain no more than 6,000 strategic nuclear warheads. But Gorbachev made a precondition for negotiations on reducing offensive nuclear weapons – that the USSR and the USA 'renounce the development, testing and deployment of space-strike weapons'.

At the beginning of the first stage the USSR and the USA would agree to stop all nuclear testing. During this time the British and French would be allowed to keep their strategic nuclear forces but not increase them. In the second stage, 'which should start no later than 1990 and last five to seven years', the other nuclear-weapon powers, presumably including China, will join the negotiations on nuclear disarmament. During this stage, the superpowers would continue to carry out the reductions in strategic nuclear weapons agreed in the first stage and negotiate away their tactical nuclear weapons, here defined as weapons having a range, or radius of action, of up to 1,000 kilometres (625 miles). In the third and final stage of nuclear disarmament, to begin no later than 1995, all remaining nuclear weapons would be eliminated. The Gorbachev plan calls for the completion of negotiations by the year 2000.

The Reagan–Gorbachev summit undoubtedly improved the atmosphere for arms control negotiations between the two superpowers. President Reagan has modified his excessively hawkish statements about the Soviet Union and General-Secretary Gorbachev has introduced a more sophisticated approach. In fact, Gorbachev is much more likely to bring off a treaty with the US than any Soviet leader since Brezhnev.

Between the end of 1979 and the summit, the superpowers were engaged in a propaganda war in which each side's proposals, however reasonable, were rejected out of hand by the other side. Proposals and counter-proposals were made more to influence public opinion than to establish serious negotiating positions. But this may now have changed. Although there may still be a propaganda component in statements about arms control and disarmament, as there almost certainly is in elements of the recent Gorbachev plan to eliminate nuclear weapons, the leaders on both sides seem intent on taking the negotiations seriously. They are, for example, both conscious of the need for some progress to be made before the next summit in the USA later this year if the meeting is to be a success. And it is important to both leaders, for domestic political reasons, that it is a success.

The negotiating positions of the two sides at Geneva on strategic nuclear forces and intermediate-range nuclear forces have serious differences, but they are close enough to give some hope that agreement in these areas could be reached. Both sides accept the need for big reductions – around 50 per cent – in their nuclear arsenals. The status of American 'forward-based' systems in Europe – particularly aircraft with the range to deliver nuclear weapons onto targets in Soviet territory – is an issue. The Soviets argue that these should count as American strategic nuclear weapon systems; the Americans regard them as tactical. Verification measures to ensure that the parties fulfil their obligations under an agreement are always contentious. The Reagan Administration in particular makes stringent verification demands. The Soviets, on the other hand, have always resisted intrusive verification measures – especially on-site inspection, which requires that inspectors go to a party's facilities to check physically that no treaty violations are taking place.

The negotiators should be able to compromise on all these differences given the political will to achieve agreement. It now seems possible that the Soviets are prepared to consider some on-site inspection; they have indicated this recently on several occasions. The January 1986 Gorbachev statement, for example, specifically states that 'verification of the destruction or limitation of arms should be carried out both by national technical means [i.e. mainly satellites] and through on-site inspections'.

Until recently, the Soviets have insisted that each of the three areas under negotiation at Geneva – strategic nuclear weapons, intermediate-range nuclear weapons and space weapons – should be linked. Progress in one area would be impossible without progress in the other two. Recent Soviet statements, however, have suggested that an agreement on intermediate-range nuclear forces in Europe, including the Soviet SS missiles and the American Pershing-II and ground-launched cruise missiles – perhaps even eliminating them – might be possible without it having a direct link with strategic and space weapons. In fact, the negotiation of such an agreement is, on current evidence, the most likely one, although the British and French nuclear forces may be stumbling blocks. The British and French governments are adamant that their strategic nuclear forces should not be included in any negotiations until the US and USSR have considerably reduced their nuclear arsenals. Moreover, these countries are anxious that their plans to modernize their strategic nuclear forces (*see* Chapter 4) are not constrained by an agreement between the superpowers. The Soviets not surprisingly count British and French strategic nuclear forces as part of the West's intermediate-range nuclear forces deployed in Europe.

But the Soviets always make one condition absolute so far as reductions in strategic nuclear weapons are concerned: the US *must* give up any testing, development and deployment of ballistic missile defences, other than those allowed by the ABM Treaty. This condition was repeated for worldwide consumption in Gorbachev's proposal for nuclear disarmament: 'Instead of wasting the next 10 to 15 years by developing new, extremely dangerous weapons in space – allegedly designed to make nuclear arms useless – would it not be more sensible to start the elimination of those arms and finally bring them down to zero?' But so far President Reagan has been adamant. Under no circumstances will he give up SDI. It is simply not negotiable, he says. And so there is an impasse. It need not be insoluble, however, provided that American Star Wars activities do not go beyond the laboratory research stage and that the Soviets are convinced that the Americans do not intend that they should.

Given that the superpowers see each other as adversaries, it is very difficult, to say the least, to see how reductions in strategic nuclear weapons can be negotiated while ballistic missile defences are being developed and deployed. The most obvious counter-measure to a ballistic missile defence is to deploy more strategic nuclear warheads, saturating the other side's defences. The Soviets are therefore most unlikely to contemplate reducing their offensive nuclear arsenal so long as the Americans persist with Star Wars. The Soviets will almost certainly assume that their adversary's motive in developing and deploying ballistic missile defences is to acquire strategic nuclear superiority through a first-strike advantage. American reassurances, such as President Reagan's statement of 31 October 1985 that the US goal was 'deep cuts, no first-strike advantage, defensive research – because defense is safer than offense', are not likely to be believed.

The sum total of all this is that the Soviets will perceive an American ballistic missile defence as part of a first-strike nuclear force. They are not likely to believe that the US will change its nuclear policy from one based on offensive forces to one based just on nuclear defence, once that defence system is operational. And, in an effort to maintain strategic offensive nuclear parity, the Soviets will subsequently increase their strategic offensive forces. This is why the Soviets insist on linkage between strategic nuclear weapons and space weapons in negotiations for reduction. And why the prospects for far-reaching strategic arms control are bleak.

Chapter 4

Star Wars and Europe

Most Europeans used to believe that the presence of some 300,000 US troops in Western Europe was enough to guarantee early American involvement in any future war in Europe. It was thought that this commitment would include, if necessary, the willingness to risk the loss of American cities in an all-out nuclear war. In the experts' jargon, the American troops were believed to 'couple' America's strategic nuclear forces to a European conflict, a coupling that has been a crucial element of the Atlantic Alliance and of NATO policy.

In the late 1970s doubts began to grow about the continued strength of this commitment, culminating in a request made by European political leaders, particularly West German Chancellor Schmidt, that the Americans deploy Pershing-II missiles in West Germany. The idea was that if there was a war in Europe, Pershing-II missiles would be fired and their warheads would explode on Soviet territory. The Soviets would not be able to distinguish Pershing-II warheads fired from West Germany from ICBM warheads fired from the US, and would retaliate by firing nuclear missiles at the US – thereby involving America in the war. In other words, the Pershing-IIs recoupled the American 'nuclear umbrella' over Europe, at least in the minds of the Europeans who instigated the proposal.

And then came SDI. Many Europeans view this idea of a ballistic missile defence to protect the US from a Soviet nuclear attack with alarm. Would this not, they ask, really decouple America's strategic nuclear forces from a European war? If the Americans were safely defended in their homeland, would they ever consider becoming involved in another European war? Is Star Wars a sign that America's commitment to NATO is decreasing?

In an effort to calm the Europeans, the White House has emphasized that if SDI leads to a large-scale ballistic missile defence system, the Americans will make sure that it will extend far enough to protect Western Europe and that it will also cover Japan, to allay similar Japanese fears. But many Europeans are not convinced by these statements. They fear that Star Wars will, if pursued, reduce American willingness to join in a future European war. There are others who argue that strategic nuclear defences would lessen Soviet and American fears about nuclear weapons and that this would remove the deterrent to war in Europe. The superpowers could then contemplate a conventional war in Europe that would destroy the continent as throughly as would a nuclear war.

The upshot is that Star Wars, one way or another, may well weaken the Atlantic Alliance and may in time lead Western European countries to make their own security arrangements with the USSR and Eastern European countries – moves that would further weaken the NATO Alliance. In an attempt to prevent this happening, European political leaders are insisting that there must be NATO negotiations before any Star Wars weaponry is deployed. But, in spite of this, it seems that a Star Wars programme is still likely to increase European suspicions that the American commitment to NATO is decreasing.

European concern about the effects of Star Wars on the NATO Alliance is enhanced by fears that Star Wars could, as predicted by the critics, become part of an American nuclear first-strike capability with the inevitable Soviet reactions to follow. The situation is even more complicated by the fact that a large-scale Star Wars deployment may well include the deployment of some components in Europe. This would inevitably involve Europe in any ramifications Star Wars may have. In addition to these more general concerns European interest in Star Wars mainly arises from four rather more specific key issues:

—The effects of the development and deployment of American ballistic missile defences on East–West relations.
—The consequences for Europe of the injection of large sums of money by the USA into the high technologies associated with Star Wars.
—The effects on British and French strategic nuclear forces of improvements in Soviet ballistic missile defences, improvements stimulated by the American Star Wars programme.
—The possible development and deployment of tactical ballistic missile defences for use in Europe.

Star Wars and Detente

Perhaps most Western and Eastern Europeans believe that their best interests – political, social, economic and security – are served by good relations between the superpowers. Such individuals prefer detente to cold war. Given that arms control negotiations between the USA and the USSR are necessary for, and a barometer of, good relations between the two powers, it is generally believed they are worth while simply to re-establish and maintain detente between East and West – even if arms control negotiations do not succeed in stopping the nuclear arms race. In fact, given the very poor record of arms control over the past 25 years, the negotiations are often seen more as a way of managing superpower relations than of managing the arms race itself.

Arms control negotiations are seen as a major indicator of the state of superpower relations. History shows that when the negotiations go on in a reasonable atmosphere, superpower relations generally benefit. 1986 might well be a propitious year for arms control negotiations were it not for SDI. In spite of his efforts at the November 1985 summit President Reagan has totally failed to convince the Soviet leadership that the US does not aim to achieve nuclear superiority. And General-Secretary Gorbachev's opposition to Star Wars does not decrease.

In these circumstances many Europeans are asking, is it worth jeopardizing today's promising atmosphere for arms control negotiations for the sake of Star Wars – a programme that is most unlikely, even in the long term, to achieve its supposed goal of making nuclear weapons obsolete? Many would be glad if the Americans dropped Star Wars for the sake of success at the negotiations at Geneva and the improved East-West relations that would follow.

Star Wars and Hi-tech

Europeans are extremely worried about the technological challenge presented by the USA and Japan. The Americans and Japanese are generally much better than the Europeans at incorporating new technologies into products that are competitive in world markets and that produce employment at home. The high-technology gap between Europe and the US, on the one hand, and Europe and Japan, on the other, is rapidly increasing.

Many European government officials and businessmen believe that SDI will widen the gap even more, for two main reasons. First is the huge injection of funds into research on Star Wars technology; $26,000 million is planned over the five-year period from 1983 and is bound to produce considerable technological advances in computer hardware and software, sensor technologies, communications, high-energy lasers, and so on. This will give American companies a large lead in these technologies.

Secondly, Europeans are concerned that the Strategic Defense Initiative Office (SDIO) in Washington will recruit many European scientists and technologists, causing a considerable 'brain drain' that few European countries can afford. Matters are made worse by the fact that the Star Wars research programme is maturing just at a time when many European universities are facing deep cuts in funding. Consequently, many European scientists understandably find American offers of employment with large salaries and very generous research funds virtually irresistible, even though they may believe all along that Star Wars is not technically feasible.

European responses to these problems have varied considerably. Some have begun to take up the invitation to 'participate in SDI research' sent to 18 of America's allies – Australia, Belgium, Canada, Denmark, France, Greece, Israel, Italy, Japan, Luxembourg, the Netherlands, Norway, Portugal, South Korea, Spain, Turkey, and the United Kingdom and West Germany. The Americans are having bilateral talks with many of the 18 'to address the various procedural concerns and to identify areas of Strategic Defense Initiative research for possible participation, consistent with US law, security interests in protecting sensitive technology, and our obligations under the ABM Treaty'.

The SDI Office will mainly coordinate any joint activities. Normally, a contract will be awarded from the SDIO to an allied government, or government agency, usually on a competitive basis. The allied government might then sub-contract the work to its industry or to laboratories. The SDIO may also award contracts directly to allied industry or individual laboratories. Allied industry and laboratories may also work directly with American companies on SDI contracts. The Americans are also encouraging another form of cooperation. 'Allies, particularly those with more limited national research capabilities, could be invited to send selected and appropriately [security] cleared personnel who can make real contributions, to join specified US research teams in a scientific exchange program.'

The US Administration is certainly trying to rope as many NATO allies as it can into the Star Wars research programme. This is not only, or even mainly, to accelerate the research programme, but to be able to claim allied political support – particularly to bolster the Administration's case with the US Congress in the next round of requests for funds for Star Wars research.

What have been the responses to the American request for cooperation on ballistic missile defence research? France has been the most strongly opposed, while Canada, Norway and Denmark have also formally refused to cooperate. Greece is also very unenthusiastic. At the other end of the scale, in December 1985 the British Government signed an agreement to cooperate with the Americans in Star Wars research, becoming the first European country to give formal approval to the programme. British participation in SDI research will be monitored by a new liaison office specially created in the Ministry of Defence for this purpose. The memorandum of understanding signed by the UK Government covered British participation in the Strategic Defense Initiative and defined the rules under which British firms can participate. According to the American magazine *Aviation Week and Space Technology*, the first contract (worth about $285,000) is for optical computing techniques and will involve Ferranti Computer Systems and Heriot-Watt University. British concerns are hopeful that they will get contracts for work in the signal-processing elements of Star Wars and in laser technology.

The then British Secretary of Defence Michael Heseltine said the agreement with the US would give Britain 'research possibilities which we could not afford on our own in technologies that will be at the centre of tomorrow's world'. He went on to say that the agreement would 'safeguard British interests in relation to the ownership of intellectual property rights and technology transfer.' But he did not explain what large-scale civilian applications he foresaw for such Star Wars technologies as high-energy lasers, particle beams, infra-red sensors, very precisely machined large mirrors, and so on! Heseltine had hoped to get guaranteed contracts worth $1,500 million but, in the event, the agreement contains no guarantees. Britain will, according to most estimates, be lucky to get Star Wars business worth more than a hundred million dollars.

In January 1986 West Germany began negotiations to become the second European ally to join the American programme, the West German Cabinet having formally approved of a German role in American ballistic missile defence research in December 1985. Washington expects to sign an SDI agreement with West Germany by mid-March and with Italy, Japan and Israel by summer. Belgium and Spain have also said that they may undertake some research.

French opposition to SDI is long-standing. As long ago as May 1985 President François Mitterrand said that France would not cooperate with the Americans in their ballistic missile defence research programme but would instead launch a European research initiative, called Eureka. This has as its stated object 'the harnessing of Europe's undoubted strengths in ideas to meet the technological challenge from America and Japan in the market place'. The idea is to identify products with a world market potential that can best be developed with Europe on a cooperative basis, then to identify the actions needed to create a European home market as big as America and Japan for those products. Examples of major areas Eureka enthusiasts single out for collaboration are: transportation, including high-speed ground transport; the factory of the future, including robotics; and home technologies – such as home information and entertainment, and domestic appliances. The advocates of Eureka believe that it would be a more profitable use of European research resources than cooperatng with the Americans on Star Wars research.

Governments of 18 Western European countries have officially backed Eureka. These include Britain and West Germany, in spite of the support these two countries are giving to the American SDI research programme, in effect competing with Eureka. In fact, the French believe that British and West German participation in the American programme will be detrimental to Eureka. But if it becomes clear to the British and West Germans that they are unlikely to get much of a share of Star Wars work, their enthusiasm for Eureka might increase.

In November 1985 the 18 participating countries agreed to 10 Eureka projects involving companies and research laboratories in 14 countries and costing about $310 million. The projects are in areas like educational computers, lasers, robots and new materials. Although Eureka is mainly a civilian programme, it could have military applications. It is too early to say how project Eureka will develop, but unless it is successful it is hard to see how Europe will ever

144

meet the increasingly tough technological challenge presented by America and Japan. This challenge is so immense that it is simply not enough to rely on a few civilian 'spin-offs' – crumbs from the table, so to speak – from cooperation with American ballistic missile defence research.

British and French Strategic Nuclear Forces

A major concern for the British and French is that a future American deployment of ballistic missile defences, particularly a nationwide system, will stimulate the Soviets to do the same. And if the Soviets deploy a more extensive ballistic missile defence than they now have, British and French strategic nuclear forces will be less able to penetrate it and reach their targets. Because these forces are relatively small, compared to those of the United States, Soviet ballistic missile defences have considerably more effect on them than on American strategic nuclear forces.

British strategic nuclear forces are carried by SLBMs. Four Polaris strategic nuclear submarines are operating, but on average only one is stationed at sea at any one time. The others are in port; perhaps two of them undergoing refits. In theory, though, the SLBMs could be fired from the submarines' base at Faslane in the Lower Clyde, Scotland. The range of the missile is about 4,000 kilometres (2,500 miles) – enough to reach Moscow from Faslane. Each Polaris submarine carries 16 SLBMs originally equipped with Polaris A3 warheads, but these are being replaced with new Polaris A3-TK (Chevaline) warheads. All four British strategic nuclear submarines will, according to current plans, be refitted with Chevaline warheads by mid-1987.

Each Polaris A3 missile carries three warheads; they are not MIRVs but MRVs, or Multiple Re-entry Vehicles. Whereas MIRVs are independently-targetable and can be aimed at targets hundreds of kilometres apart, MRVs are only able to separate to fall on different parts of one city. The point of MRVs is that a number of warheads exploding over areas of a city cause far more destruction than a single warhead of the same total explosive yield. Each Polaris A3 warhead has an explosive power equivalent to that of 200,000 tons of TNT.

The Chevaline system is reliably thought to carry two MRV warheads, although the British Government has not officially confirmed this. Each warhead probably has an explosive power equivalent to that of 40,000 tons of TNT. Chevaline has a greater targeting flexibility than the Polaris A3 and is better able to penetrate the Soviet ABM system around Moscow. It may achieve this extra survivability by confusing Soviet radars (by having a number of decoys with its real warheads) and by manoeuvring the 'bus' carrying the warheads and decoys during the terminal phase of the flight path.

The British intend to replace their four Polaris submarines with Trident submarines carrying Trident-II missiles. The Tridents should be operational in the 1990s when the hulls of the Polaris submarines, their weakest part, will be worn out. The Trident programme is expensive. The estimated total cost of the four-submarine fleet is at least £11,000 million ($15,000 million). These expenditures will be spread over a number of years but annual costs of the Trident programme in the late 1980s will exceed £1,000 million, a significant fraction of the British military budget, which is currently about £18,000 million. Only a fraction of this budget (about 30 per cent) is for buying weapons and equipment, so the Trident programme will mean far less money for British conventional military forces, a source of concern to many.

The Trident-II missile can carry 14 MIRVed warheads. This means that the four British strategic nuclear submarines will be able theoretically to carry a total of 896 independently-targetable warheads. But the British Government has said that it will not put more than eight warheads on each Trident-II missile, giving a total of 512 warheads. Presumably, the rest of the payload will be taken up by decoys and other penetration aids. Missiles can be fired from no more than two of the four British strategic nuclear submarines (the other two are normally undergoing refits), so the maximum number of British Trident-II warheads available to attack Soviet targets will be 256, compared with today's 32.

But, perhaps more important than the quantitative increase in warhead number is the qualitative change gleaned from the switch to Trident. Trident-II warheads are far more accurate than Polaris warheads.

It is arguable whether or not the British have an independent nuclear deterrent, as they claim. The British strategic nuclear forces are well-integrated into the American strategic nuclear targeting plans, and though the British could theoretically fire their nuclear weapons independently of the Americans, they are, to say the least, most unlikely to do so in practice. Moreover, one or two British submarines at sea would, on their own, be no match for Soviet anti-submarine warfare systems.

Britain's role as a nuclear-weapon power would be greatly reduced if the Soviets deployed an extensive ballistic missile defence system. The credibility of the British nuclear deterrent would virtually vanish. For this reason, British Prime Minister Margaret Thatcher agreed the following four points with President Reagan at a meeting at Camp David in

December 1984:

—The United States and Western aim is not to achieve superiority, but to maintain balance, taking account of Soviet developments.
—Strategic Defense Initiative-related deployment would, in view of treaty obligations, have to be a matter for negotiation.
—The overall aim is to enhance, not to undercut, deterrence.
—East/West negotiations should aim to achieve security with reduced levels of offensive systems on both sides. This will be the purpose of the resumed United States/Soviet negotiations on arms control.

These points are a good summary of the attitudes of most European NATO Governments to Star Wars. What support there is for the American programme is at best lukewarm and given more for the sake of maintaining the Atlantic Alliance than as an indicator of real enthusiasm.

The British attitude is somewhat complicated by a desire to keep up 'the special relationship' with the USA and therefore to be seen solidly to back the American President, particularly when other European NATO Governments are less than supportive. This led the Prime Minister to persuade former Secretary of Defence Heseltine to sign the agreement on cooperating with the SDIO. But it has not stopped Foreign Secretary Geoffrey Howe and other ministers expressing grave doubts about SDI. Thus, in his speech at the Royal United Services Institute on 15 March 1985, Sir Geoffrey said:

It would be wrong to underestimate the enormous technological expertise and potential of the United States; but, as we all recognize, there would be no advantage in creating a new Maginot Line of the twenty-first century, liable to be outflanked by relatively simpler and demonstrably cheaper counter-measures. If the technology does work, what will be its psychological impact on the other side? President Reagan has repeatedly made clear that he does not seek superiority. But we would have to ensure that the perceptions of others were not different.

Sir Geoffrey went on to ask:

If it initially proved feasible to construct only limited [ballistic missiles] defences, these would be bound to be more vulnerable than comprehensive systems to countermeasures. Would these holes in the dyke produce and even encourage a nuclear flood? Leaving aside the threat to civilian populations would active defences provide the only feasible way of protecting key military installations? Might we be better advised to employ other methods of protection, such as more mobile and under-sea forces?

These rhetorical questions, like the views expressed by other ministers, clearly show the British concern for the effect of ballistic missile defences on British strategic nuclear forces. This concern causes them to argue strongly against any weakening or restrictive interpretation of the ABM Treaty and in favour of negotiations to reduce the strategic offensive arsenals of the Soviets and the Americans.

The French, with no perceived 'special relationship' with the Americans to think about, are much more publicly critical of President Reagan's SDI than the British. The French Defence Minister, Paul Quiles, said of Star Wars: 'The most optimistic predictions do not allow us to consider this a credible project, even for the next half-century. Science can make progress, sometimes very rapid progress, but it cannot work miracles.' Like Sir Geoffrey Howe,

Quiles warned that 'A space defence risks becoming a new Maginot Line more costly than all such previous military projects.'

French objections to large-scale ballistic missile defences are also based on the effect that increased Soviet defences will have on French strategic nuclear forces. As with the UK, these forces are relatively small compared to the huge arsenals of the USA and USSR. The French strategic nuclear forces consist of 18 S3 land-based ground-to-ground missiles and 96 SLBMs. Each S3 missile carries a single nuclear warhead with an explosive power equal to that of 1 million tons of TNT. The missiles are based in underground silos located on the Plateau d'Albion in Haute Provence. With a range of 3,500 kilometres (2,200 miles), they can hit targets in any part of the USSR west of the Urals.

Eighty of the French SLBMs are M-20 missiles, each carrying a single warhead with the same explosive power as the S3 warhead. The other 16 SLBMs are M-4 missiles, each carrying six MIRVs with an explosive power equivalent to that of 150,000 tons of TNT. The range of the M-20 SLBM is 3,000 kilometres (1,875 miles); that of the M-4 is 4,000 kilometres (2,500 miles). The French Navy operates six strategic nuclear submarines, each carrying 16 SLBMs. The M-4 SLBM will be backfitted on all but one of these. This modernization programme will increase the number of SLBM warheads from 80 in 1984 to 496 by 1993, although, like the British, the French can fire at most a half of their SLBMs at any one time. In addition, the French are developing an air-to-surface missile, the ASMP, to be deployed in a strategic role on 18 Mirage-IV aircraft, starting in 1986.

Given the very expensive modernization programme for their strategic nuclear forces – including the development of a mobile ground-to-ground missile to replace the S3 and a new SLBM, both for deployment in the mid-1990s – the French are anxious to keep Soviet ballistic missile defences to a minimum. They therefore oppose any American actions likely to stimulate the development and deployment of Soviet nuclear defences.

Tactical Anti-ballistic Missiles

The enormous attention given since 1983 to SDI has, not very surprisingly, stimulated discussion about possibly using tactical anti-ballistic missile systems in Europe to attack enemy short-range and intermediate-range ballistic missiles. The discussion is topical because both the USA and USSR are in the process of deploying surface-to-air missiles (the American Patriot, the Soviet SA-X-12) which could be given a tactical anti-ballistic missile capability.

The Patriot is a very sophisticated anti-aircraft missile now replacing Nike-Hercules, and deployed in a number of NATO countries. Most Nike-Hercules missiles are equipped with nuclear warheads; Patriot missiles carry conventional fragmentation warheads, weighing about 75 kilograms (167 pounds). The deployment of Patriot began in the Netherlands in 1984. The satisfaction the US Army has with the Patriot is shown by its plan to buy 6,200 of the missiles to set up 81 batteries. Fifty-four of them are scheduled for deployment in Europe by the early 1990s.

Patriot took the Americans 17 years to develop and is undoubtedly a remarkable weapon. It is relatively large: 5 metres (5½ yards) long and 41 centimetres (16 inches) in diameter, it weighs about 1,000 kilograms (2,222 pounds) at launch. The system is not cheap; about 500 missiles and 12 fire units cost $1,000 million. But whereas units of Nike-Hercules missiles can identify, track and engage only one enemy aircraft at a time, a Patriot battery can keep track of 100 aircraft and engage nine of them with nine different missiles at the same time. The key to Patriot's performance is its phased-array radar that gives early warning of attack, tracks hostile aircraft, fires the missiles at the appropriate moments and guides the missiles accurately to their targets. Most of these tasks are automated; all certainly could be.

The central computer in the Patriot system analyses the data from the radar; the computer fires the missiles and controls their interceptions with enemy aircraft. The radar continuously monitors the situation, tracking the aircraft and the attacking missiles. Each missile carries a sensor that is aimed towards the enemy aircraft by the ground-based radar; this guides the missile to the target. The missile travels to the target at a maximum speed of about six times the speed of sound, and a cruising speed of about half this maximum. Its maximum range is about 80 kilometres (50 miles) and it can intercept aircraft flying at altitudes up to 25 kilometres (15 miles).

A Patriot battery consists of a fire control station with eight launchers each having four missiles, a maintenance section, and a decoy unit to protect the battery against enemy missiles homing in on the radiation emitted by Patriot's radars. Only the control station containing the computer is manned. A Patriot battery can be operated by, at most, 12 people. Patriots are normally deployed in battalions of six batteries plus the battalion command post.

Experts believe that Patriot could be given a tactical anti-ballistic missile capability. Although missile warheads travel at much faster speeds than aircraft, they are usually not manoeuvrable, or at least not very manoeuvrable, and this helps a surface-to-air missile to intercept them. W.A. Smit, a Dutch missile expert, argues that Patriot could be given the capability to intercept enemy tactical ballistic missiles by modifying the computer software for detection, tracking and guidance. He explains:

Consider the Soviet SS-22 missile, whose warhead re-enters the atmosphere at a speed of three kilometres [1.8 miles] per second. The Patriot's radar has a range of 150 kilometres [94 miles]. The SS-22 warhead takes 50 seconds to cover this distance. If the radar and computer software take less than 10 seconds to detect, identify and calculate the trajectory of the SS-22, the Patriot missiles would still have 40 seconds to intercept the enemy warhead. The Patriot missile could cover about eight kilometres [5 miles] during the time, about 12 seconds, that its booster is burning. At that moment, the Patriot and the SS-22 warhead are still about 80 kilometres [50 miles] apart – a distance that would be bridged in about 20 seconds. With suitable software changes and modified guidance rules, such a time schedule does not seem to be a major obstacle. Either the Patriot's present fragmentation warhead or a modified version might be used for the destruction of the SS-22 warhead.

In a similar fashion it can be shown that the Soviet SA-12 surface-to-air missile could be given a tactical anti-ballistic missile capability.

To say that the Patriot has a tactical anti-ballistic missile capability against Soviet missiles like the SS-20, the SS-21, -22 and -23, fired over distances of less than 3,000 kilometres (1,875 miles) or so, does not mean that it could intercept ICBM warheads, which have a much faster re-entry velocity. But Patriot would probably be able to intercept the warheads of Soviet SLBMs when fired over distances of less than 3,000 kilometres (1,875 miles). And it is this capability that might be said to violate the ABM Treaty –

although this treaty deals with *strategic*, rather than tactical, anti-ballistic missiles. Others will argue that a modified Patriot or a Soviet SA-X-12 is not an ABM as defined by the ABM Treaty, because it does not have a complete strategic ABM capability.

The ABM Treaty clearly has a loop-hole concerning the modification of surface-to-air missiles to tactical anti-ballistic missiles. And many believe that the ABM Treaty should be strengthened by closing this loop-hole.

An argument given for European cooperation in American SDI research is that experience will be gained in the development of a new generation of tactical anti-ballistic missiles for use in Europe – a European Tactical Defence Initiative, in other words. A separate European Initiative is, however, strongly opposed by the Americans; Caspar Weinberger, for example, believes that it would be a wasteful duplication of effort and may lead to a split in the NATO Alliance, because the Americans are also looking into tactical anti-ballistic missiles.

There are other objections. A large-scale European Tactical Defence Initiative could jeopardize the ABM Treaty, be very destabilizing, be a major stimulant of the East–West arms race, seriously hinder arms control negotiations and be perceived by the Soviets as part of a quest by NATO for a pre-emptive attack – objections strongly resembling those made against SDI.

There may also be an element of 'sour grapes' in the European objections to Star Wars. Jealousy of American technological progress enhanced by Europe's relative technological decline, and a desire to hinder further American progress, may be seen as the main motives for the objections. Whether or not this is so, many Europeans still base their views of Star Wars on the conviction that a comprehensive ballistic missile defence is not technically feasible in the foreseeable future.

Conclusion

Star Wars: Reality or Pie in the Sky?

Almost as soon as a weapon is invented, people begin thinking about how to counteract it. Ballistic missiles are no exception. Soon after they were deployed, research began into ways of intercepting them before they reached their targets. Both the Americans and the Soviets have had active research programmes into ballistic missile defence systems since the early 1950s.

President Reagan's Strategic Defense Initiative is not an exotic new research programme. Rather it is an attempt to coordinate and accelerate research on ballistic missile defence systems already under way in many research laboratories across the United States. The aim of the President's Initiative is to discover, within the next five years or so, the potential of various technologies (such as high-energy lasers, including X-ray lasers, particle beams, kinetic-energy weapons, and so on) for the interception and destruction in flight of enemy ballistic missiles, or their warheads, and the technical feasibility of President Reagan's vision – the protection of the entire American population against an all-out Soviet ballistic missile attack.

What is new is that research into ballistic missile defence now has the very strong personal backing of the American President. This gives ballistic missile defence efforts prestige and an importance that their protagonists did not have before 23 March 1983. And the President is making sure that the research is receiving much more money than it would otherwise have done. Star Wars activities have been promised $30,000 million or so in the five-year period from Fiscal Year 1985 to Fiscal Year 1989, inclusive. The President will do all he can to protect these funds against Congressional cuts. And all the while American public spending is certainly threatened with large-scale reductions.

The Gramm-Rudman deficit reduction law requires that the White House eliminates the US budget deficit by 1991. In line with this, American military spending is expected to be slashed by about $6,000 million this year. The major military programme that suffers least is Star Wars; funding for this Fiscal year stands at $2,750 million (the original Administration's request was $3,700 million). This is almost double last year's funding of $1,400 million and about three times the funding approved two years ago ($951 million). In the next Fiscal Year beginning in October 1986, Star Wars research cash will probably almost double this year's spending, in spite of the Gramm-Rudman cuts. President Reagan is determined that his investment in ballistic missile defence research will not be slashed. The President's prestige is at stake.

This all means big money to American industry. Almost all of the money for SDI is likely to go to American companies. The value of contracts going to European firms, for example, will probably be no more than about $300 million over five years – about one per cent of the total. In Fiscal Years 1983 and 1984, five American firms – Boeing, Rockwell International, TRW, Lockheed and McDonnell Douglas – shared more than $1,000 million in contracts for ballistic missile defence. In Fiscal Year 1985 these firms received a further $360 million, excluding long-term contracts like Boeing's five-year $289-million award for an airborne optical system.

These companies and others who receive big money for Star Wars research will want to make sure that their research investment leads to the large-scale deployment of ballistic missile defence systems – where the really big money is. As Senator William Proxmire said in the *New York Times* on 5 November 1985, these corporations 'look at SDI as an insurance policy that will maintain their prosperity for the next two decades'. No wonder that British Foreign Secretary Sir Geoffrey Howe warned that 'research may acquire an unstoppable momentum of its own, even though the case for stopping may strengthen with the passage of years. Prevention may be better than later attempts at a cure. We must take care that political decisions are not pre-empted by the march of technology.'

Given the huge vested interests in the development and deployment of Star Wars weapons systems now growing among the many large American corporations involved in Star Wars business, the large number of scientists who are becoming dependent on Star Wars research money, and the large bureaucracy that will administer Star Wars activities, it will be extremely difficult to stop some deployment of ballistic missile defences. This will be so even if the next American President is less keen on Star Wars than President Reagan; it is most unlikely that any President will be able to resist the pressure applied by the huge vested interests in Star Wars. Ironically, the military in general have shown little enthusiasm for the programme, although the Pentagon supports the President's wishes on Star Wars. Many military men are mindful of cuts in military budgets and would prefer that the money going on Star Wars was spent on other things. The driving force behind SDI is therefore an industrial-academic-bureaucratic complex rather than the usual military-industrial-academic-bureaucratic complex.

If some deployment of ballistic missile defences is virtually inevitable, what sort of deployment is most likely? The vast majority of those commenting on Star Wars, whether advocates or critics, are sceptical about the feasibility of an effective nationwide defence against ballistic missile attack, making nuclear weapons eventually 'impotent and obsolete'. Many of the Star Wars technologies being considered present enormous, in some cases seemingly insurmountable, challenges. And already the Achilles' heel of Star Wars is turning out to be the computer software.

No one knows yet the computer capacity required for Star Wars, because the scope of the defence system has not been decided. But computer experts estimate (or, more correctly, guess) that 10 to 30 million lines of code (instructions to the computers) would be required for a total ballistic missile defence system. Moreover, the computer programme would have to be virtually error-free. A task of this magnitude has not yet been undertaken; according to computer expert Herbert Lin, 'no software-engineering technology can be anticipated that will support the goal of a comprehensive ballistic-missile defense'. Another computer expert, Ware Myers, said: 'these enormous software systems are by far the most complex intellectual constructions that the human mind has attempted. It is small wonder that we have not yet learned to build them without errors.'

Star Wars advocates, of course, have another point of view. General Daniel O. Graham claims that 'such problems were solved years ago. We have satellites systems now which have operated for over 10 years and whose computers have handled more than a billion computations per second. The Space Shuttle requires seven million lines of software code; AT&T [the US telephone company] uses a switching system that requires 50 million lines. Further, US data handling capability has been increasing 10-fold every four years.' The issue took a dramatic turn on 29 June 1985, when David L. Parnas resigned as a member of the SDI Organization's Panel on Computing in Support of Battle Management. 'If you gave me the job of building the [computer-software] system, and all the resources that I wanted, I could not do it,' he wrote. 'I don't expect the next 20 years of research to change that fact.'

It sometimes seems that President Reagan is the only person who now believes in a nationwide system and is sticking to his vision. Even the director of the SDIO, General James Abrahamson, has admitted that 'a perfect astrodome defense is not a realistic thing'. And a Pentagon official, Richard Sybert, who is Special Assistant to the Secretary of Defense, has written of SDI: 'No one has ever said such a system could or would be 100 per cent effective'.

What now seems much more on the cards is the deployment of ballistic missile defences around ICBM silos, Trident strategic nuclear submarine bases, major air bases used by strategic bombers and military command centres. Once again, there is nothing new about this. It is well known that by the 1983 announcement, the Americans had done much research on silo-defence systems. One such system, called the Low Altitude Defense System, or LOADS, uses an anti-ballistic missile evolved from the Sprint missile, using a low-yield enhanced-radiation warhead ('neutron bomb') to intercept attacking Soviet warheads at altitudes of about 1.5 kilometres (1 mile). The Pentagon is keen to use such a system to defend its new MX ICBMs scheduled for deployment in fixed silos.

Some people believe that the main point of the American programme is really to provoke the Soviets to follow suit. The financial cost to both sides of a virtually open-ended arms race in space would be huge and it is thought that the USSR would be less able to afford it than the USA. The result would be an economic war that the Americans would win. But others are not so sure who the winner would be.

The future evolution of nuclear policies will certainly be complex. Technological advances in nuclear weapons, particularly increased accuracy of delivery, are changing nuclear policies from nuclear deterrence based on mutual assured destruction (a policy based on the targeting of cities) to nuclear warfighting – a policy that emphasizes military targets. It is feared by many that this change will increase the probability of nuclear war, because it encourages the notion that nuclear war is 'fightable and winnable'.

Another alarming change in nuclear policies will occur when anti-submarine warfare technologies succeed in significantly limiting the damage that can be done by submarine-launched ballistic missiles, which are currently far less vulnerable to a sudden attack than are land-based ICBMs. Effective anti-submarine warfare, together with ballistic missile defences and anti-satellite warfare systems, could lead to one side believing that it could gain an advantage by making a sudden attack on the other side's strategic nuclear forces. Those nuclear forces that survived the first strike could then be dealt with by the attacker's ballistic missile defence system. A partial defence system, even one meant to defend strategic nuclear forces against a ballistic missile attack by the other side, might be just about adequate for this purpose.

The adoption of this nuclear-war-winning policy would again make a nuclear world war more likely. And it may turn out that the most important effect of Star Wars on world security is the role (or the role perceived by the Soviets) of American ballistic missile defences in a nuclear first strike.

It can be argued that, come what may, Soviet strategists are at some stage bound to interpret the American deployment of ballistic missile defences as part of an American attempt to acquire a nuclear first-strike capability – even if the Americans don't mean it that way. The vital question then arises as to whether the Soviets could afford to let this happen. They may decide not to accept a change in the current situation of strategic nuclear parity, particularly if it reduces them to a state of nuclear inferiority. Rather than accept this, the Soviets may decide to make a nuclear attack on the USA before the Americans deploy a significant ballistic missile defence system. So President Reagan's Initiative could bring on the nuclear world war it was designed to prevent. It goes without saying that exactly the same argument applies to the deployment of a significant new Soviet ballistic missile defence system, and its consequences.

As far as arms control is concerned, the crunch will come when ballistic missile defence activities threaten the ABM Treaty. The Soviets seem to accept that research is a process that cannot be easily controlled, and are prepared to agree that even research into ballistic missile defence should not prevent negotiations about reducing offensive strategic nuclear weapons. The problem is in defining research. If it goes beyond the laboratory stage into testing, the ABM Treaty will be in jeopardy and the Soviets are unlikely to want to continue negotiating reductions in strategic offensive nuclear weapons.

If you believe that Star Wars will destabilize the strategic relationship between the superpowers and may become an element in a nuclear first-strike policy, that it may lead to an unrestrained nuclear arms race on Earth and in space – wasting a large fraction of the world's scarce scientific, technological and financial resources – then you will feel that the following three steps are necessary to prevent these consequences:

1. Strict adherence to the ABM Treaty as originally interpreted. This means no testing of ballistic missile defence components.
2. The preservation of the limits on strategic nuclear forces defined in the SALT II Treaty, until considerable reductions in strategic nuclear forces (of the sort already tabled by the superpowers at Geneva) can be negotiated. Because the negotiation of deep cuts in strategic nuclear weapons will be a lengthy process, an obvious (and possibly achievable) first step would be the negotiation of a verified freeze on the testing, production and deployment of nuclear weapons.
3. The negotiation of a ban on the testing and deployment of anti-satellite weapons.

It has been pointed out that the high-energy lasers being considered as Star Wars weapons could be used to set fire to enemy cities. According to a recent study: 'in a matter of hours a laser defense system powerful enough to cope with the ballistic missile threat can also destroy the enemy's major cities by fire. The attack would proceed city by city, the attack time for each city being only a matter of minutes. Not nuclear destruction, but Armageddon all the same.' It will be a supreme irony if Star Wars weapons turn out to be just more weapons of mass devastation, competing in destructiveness with the nuclear weapons they are designed to destroy.

Appendix A

The Conclusion of President Reagan's Speech

23 March 1983

Now, thus far tonight I've shared with you my thoughts on the problems of national security we must face together. My predecessors in the Oval Office have appeared before you on other occasions to describe the threat posed by Soviet power and have proposed steps to address that threat. But since the advent of nuclear weapons, those steps have been increasingly directed toward deterrence of aggression through the promise of retaliation.

This approach to stability through offensive threat has worked. We and our allies have succeeded in preventing nuclear war for more than three decades. In recent months, however, my advisers, including in particular the Joint Chiefs of Staff, have underscored the necessity to break out of a future that relies solely on offensive retaliation for our security.

Over the course of these discussions, I've become more and more deeply convinced that the human spirit must be capable of rising above dealing with other nations and human beings by threatening their existence. Feeling this way, I believe we must thoroughly examine every opportunity for reducing tensions and for introducing greater stability into the strategic calculus on both sides.

One of the most important contributions we can

make is, of course, to lower the level of all arms, and particularly nuclear arms. We're engaged right now in several negotiations with the Soviet Union to bring about a mutual reduction of weapons. I will report to you a week from tomorrow my thoughts on that score. But let me just say, I'm totally committed to this course.

If the Soviet Union will join with us in our effort to achieve major arms reduction, we will have succeeded in stabilizing the nuclear balance. Nevertheless, it will still be necessary to rely on the specter of retaliation, on mutual threat. And that's a sad commentary on the human condition. Wouldn't it be better to save lives than to avenge them? Are we not capable of demonstrating our peaceful intentions by applying all our abilities and our ingenuity to achieving a truly lasting stability? I think we are. Indeed, we must.

After careful consultation with my advisers, including the Joint Chiefs of Staff, I believe there is a way. Let me share with you a vision of the future which offers hope. It is that we embark on a program to counter the awesome Soviet missile threat with measures that are defensive. Let us turn to the very strengths in technology that spawned our great industrial base and that have given us the quality of life we enjoy today.

What if free people could live secure in the knowledge that their security did not rest upon the threat of instant US retaliation to deter a Soviet attack, that we could intercept and destroy strategic ballistic missiles before they reached our own soil or that of our allies?

I know this is a formidable, technical task, one that may not be accomplished before the end of this century. Yet, current technology has attained a level of sophistication where it's reasonable for us to begin this effort. It will take years, probably decades of effort on many fronts. There will be failures and setbacks, just as there will be successes and breakthroughs. And as we proceed, we must remain constant in preserving the nuclear deterrent and maintaining a solid capability for flexible response. But isn't it worth every investment necessary to free the world from the threat of nuclear war? We know it is.

In the meantime, we will continue to pursue real reductions in nuclear arms, negotiating from a position of strength that can be ensured only by modernizing our strategic forces. At the same time, we must take steps to reduce the risk of a conventional military conflict escalating to nuclear war by improving our non-nuclear capabilities.

America does possess – now – the technologies to attain very significant improvements in the effectiveness of our conventional, non-nuclear forces. Proceeding boldly with these new technologies, we can significantly reduce any incentive that the Soviet Union may have to threaten attack against the United States or its allies.

As we pursue our goal of defensive technologies, we recognize that our allies rely upon our strategic offensive power to deter attacks against them. Their vital interests and ours are inextricably linked. Their safety and ours are one. And no change in technology can or will alter that reality. We must and shall continue to honor our commitments.

I clearly recognize that defensive systems have limitations and raise certain problems and ambiguities. If paired with offensive systems, they can be viewed as fostering an aggressive policy, and no one wants that. But with these considerations firmly in mind, I call upon the scientific community in our country, those who gave us nuclear weapons, to turn their great talents now to the cause of mankind and world peace, to give us the means of rendering these nuclear weapons impotent and obsolete.

Tonight, consistent with our obligations of the ABM Treaty and recognizing the need for closer consultation with our allies, I'm taking an important first step. I am directing a comprehensive and intensive effort to define a long-term research and development program to begin to achieve our ultimate goal of eliminating the threat posed by strategic nuclear missiles. This could pave the way for arms control measures to eliminate the weapons themselves. We seek neither military superiority nor political advantage. Our only purpose – one all people share – is to search for ways to reduce the danger of nuclear war.

My fellow Americans, tonight we're launching an effort which holds the promise of changing the course of human history. There will be risks, and results take time. But I believe we can do it. As we cross this threshold, I ask for your prayers and your support.

Thank you, good night, and God bless you.

Appendix B

Statement by Mikhail Gorbachev

15 January 1986

A new year, 1986, has begun. It will be an important year, one might say a turning point in the history of the Soviet state, the year of the 27th Congress of the CPSU. The Congress will chart the guidelines for the political, social, economic and intellectual development of Soviet society in the period up to the next millennium. It will adopt a programme for accelerating our peaceful construction.

All efforts of the CPSU are directed towards ensuring a further improvement of the life of the Soviet people.

A turn for the better is also needed on the international scene. This is the expectation and the demand of the peoples of the Soviet Union and of the peoples throughout the world.

Being aware of this, at the very start of the new year the Political Bureau of the CPSU Central Committee and the Soviet Government have adopted a decision on a number of major foreign policy measures that are of a fundamental nature. They are designed to promote to a maximum degree an improvement of the international situation. They are prompted by the need to overcome the negative confrontational tendencies that have been growing in recent years and to clear the ways towards curbing the nuclear arms race on earth and preventing it in outer space, towards an overall reduction of the war danger and towards confidence-building as an integral part of relations among states.

I

The most important of these measures is a concrete programme aimed at the complete elimination of nuclear weapons throughout the world within a precisely defined period of time.

The Soviet Union proposes that a step-by-step, consistent process of ridding the earth of nuclear weapons be implemented and completed within the next 15 years, before the end of this century.

The 20th century has given mankind the gift of the energy of the atom. However, this great achievement of the human intellect can turn into an instrument of mankind's self-annihilation.

Is it possible to resolve this contradiction? We are convinced that it is possible. Finding effective ways of eliminating nuclear weapons is a feasible task, provided it is tackled without delay.

The Soviet Union proposes that a programme of ridding mankind of the fear of a nuclear catastrophe be carried out beginning in 1986. The fact that this year has been proclaimed by the United Nations the International Year of Peace provides an additional political and moral stimulus for this. What is required here is that we should rise above national selfishness, tactical considerations, differences and disputes, whose significance is nothing compared to the preservation of what is most cherished – peace and a secure future. The energy of the atom should be placed solely at the service of peace, a goal that our socialist state has consistently pursued and continues to pursue.

Our country was the first to raise, back in 1946, the question of prohibiting the production and use of atomic weapons and to make nuclear energy serve peaceful purposes, for the benefit of mankind.

How does the Soviet Union envisage today in practical terms the process of reducing nuclear weapons, both delivery vehicles and warheads, up to their complete elimination? Our proposals on this subject can be summarized as follows.

Stage One. Within the next five to eight years the USSR and the USA will reduce by one half the nuclear weapons that can reach each other's territory. As for the remaining delivery vehicles of this kind, each side will retain no more than 6,000 warheads.

It stands to reason that such a reduction is possible only if both the USSR and the USA renounce the development, testing and deployment of space-strike weapons. As the Soviet Union has repeatedly warned, the development of space-strike weapons will dash the hopes for a reduction of nuclear armaments on earth.

The first stage will include the adoption and implementation of a decision on the complete elimination of medium-range missiles of the USSR and the USA in the European zone – both ballistic and cruise missiles – as a first step towards ridding the European continent of nuclear weapons.

At the same time the United States should undertake not to transfer its strategic and medium-range missiles to other countries, while Britain and France should pledge not to build up their respective nuclear arsenals.

The USSR and the USA should from the very beginning agree to stop all nuclear explosions and call upon other states to join in such a moratorium as soon as possible.

The reason why the first stage of nuclear disarmament should concern the Soviet Union and the United States is that it is they who should set an example for the other nuclear powers. We said that very frankly to President Reagan of the United States during our meeting in Geneva.

Stage Two. At this stage, which should start no later than 1990 and last for five to seven years, the other nuclear powers will begin to join the process of nuclear disarmament. To start with, they would pledge to freeze all their nuclear arms and not to have them on the territories of other countries.

In this period the USSR and the USA will continue to carry out the reductions agreed upon during the first stage and also implement further measures aimed at eliminating their medium-range nuclear weapons and freezing their tactical nuclear systems.

Following the completion by the USSR and the USA of a 50-per-cent reduction of their respective armaments at the second stage, another radical step will be taken: all nuclear powers will eliminate their tactical nuclear weapons, i.e. weapons having a range (or radius of action) of up to 1,000 kilometres.

At this stage the Soviet-US accord on the prohibition of space-strike weapons would become multilateral, with the mandatory participation in it of major industrial powers.

All nuclear powers would stop nuclear weapon tests.

There would be a ban on the development of non-nuclear weapons based on new physical principles, whose destructive power is close to that of nuclear arms or other weapons of mass destruction.

Stage Three will begin no later than 1995. At this stage the elimination of all remaining nuclear weapons will be completed. By the end of 1999 there will be no nuclear weapons on earth. A universal accord will be drawn up that such weapons should never again come into being.

We envisage that special procedures will be worked out for the destruction of nuclear weapons as well as for the dismantling, re-equipment or scrapping of delivery vehicles. In the process, agreement will be reached on the number of weapons to be scrapped at each stage, the sites of their destruction and so on.

Verification of the destruction or limitation of arms should be carried out both by national technical means and through on-site inspections. The USSR is ready to reach agreement on any other additional verification measures.

Adoption of the nuclear disarmament programme that we are proposing would unquestionably have a favourable impact on the negotiations conducted at bilateral and multilateral forums. The programme would envisage clearly-defined routes and reference points, establish a specific timetable for achieving agreements and implementing them and would make the negotiations purposeful and task-oriented. This would stop the dangerous trend whereby the momentum of the arms race is greater than the progress of negotiations.

Thus, we propose that we should enter the third millennium without nuclear weapons, on the basis of mutually acceptable and strictly verifiable agreements. If the United States Administration is indeed committed to the goal of the complete elimination of nuclear weapons everywhere, as it has repeatedly stated, it now has a practical opportunity to carry it out in practice. Instead of spending the next 10 to 15 years in developing new space weapons, which are extremely dangerous for mankind, weapons allegedly designed to make nuclear arms unnecessary, would it not be more sensible to start eliminating those weapons and finally doing away with them altogether? The Soviet Union, I repeat, proposes precisely that.

The Soviet Union calls upon all peoples and states, and, naturally, above all nuclear states, to support the programme of eliminating nuclear weapons before the year 2000. It is absolutely clear to any unbiased person that if such a programme is implemented, nobody would lose and all stand to gain. This is a problem common to all mankind and it can and must be solved only through joint efforts. And the sooner this programme is translated into practical deeds, the safer life on our planet will be.

II

Guided by the same approach and a desire to take another practical step within the context of the nuclear disarmament programme, the Soviet Union has adopted an important decision.

We are extending by three months our unilateral moratorium on all nuclear explosions, which expired on December 31, 1985. Such a moratorium will remain in force even longer if the United States for its part also stops nuclear tests. We propose once again to the United States that it join this initiative whose significance is evident practically to everyone in the world.

Obviously the adoption of such a decision has by no means been simple for us. The Soviet Union cannot display unilateral restraint with regard to nuclear tests indefinitely. But the stakes are too high and the responsibility too great for us not to try every possibility of influencing the position of others by force of example.

All experts, scientists, politicians and military men agree that the cessation of tests would indeed reliably block the channels of perfecting nuclear weapons. And this is a top-priority task. A reduction of nuclear arsenals alone, without a prohibition of nuclear weapon tests, does not provide a way out of the dilemma of nuclear threat, since the remaining weapons would be modernized and there would still be the possibility of developing increasingly sophisticated and lethal nuclear weapons and appraising their new types at test ranges.

Therefore, the cessation of tests is a practical step

towards eliminating nuclear weapons.

I wish to say the following at the outset. Any references to verification as an obstacle to the establishment of a moratorium on nuclear explosions are totally groundless. We declare unequivocally that for us verification is not a problem. Should the United States agree to stop all nuclear explosions on a reciprocal basis, appropriate verification of compliance with the moratorium would be fully ensured by national technical means as well as with the help of international procedures including on-site inspections when necessary. We invite the United States to reach agreement with us to this effect.

The USSR resolutely stands for making the moratorium a bilateral, and later, a multilateral measure. We are also in favour of resuming the tripartite negotiations, involving the USSR, the USA and Great Britain, on the complete and general prohibition of nuclear weapon tests. This could be done immediately, even this month. We are also prepared to begin without delay multilateral test-ban negotiations within the framework of the Geneva Conference on Disarmament, with all nuclear powers taking part.

Non-aligned countries have proposed that consultations be held with the aim of extending the 1963 Moscow Treaty Banning Nuclear Weapon Tests in the Atmosphere, in Outer Space and Under Water to cover also underground tests, whose ban is not envisaged in the treaty. The Soviet Union agrees to this, too.

Since last summer we have been calling upon the United States to follow our example and stop nuclear explosions. Washington has not yet done that despite protests and demands on the part of the public, and contrary to the will of most states in the world. By carrying out more and more nuclear explosions the US side continues to pursue its elusive dream of achieving military superiority. This policy is futile and dangerous, a policy which is not worthy of the level of civilization that modern society has attained.

In the absence of a positive response from the United States, the Soviet side had every right to resume nuclear tests starting January 1, 1986. If one were to follow the usual logic of the arms race, that, presumably, would have been the thing to do.

But the whole point is that it is precisely that logic, if one can call it that, that has to be resolutely rejected. We are making yet another attempt in this direction. Otherwise the process of military rivalry will assume gigantic proportions and any control over the course of events would be impossible. To yield to the anarchic force of the nuclear arms race is impermissible. This would be acting against reason and the human instinct of self-preservation. What is required are new and bold approaches, fresh political thinking and a heightened sense of responsibility for the destinies of the peoples.

The US Administration is once again given more time to consider our proposals on stopping nuclear explosions and to give a positive answer to them. It is this kind of response that people everywhere in the world will expect from Washington.

The Soviet Union appeals to the President and Congress of the United States, to the American people: there is an opportunity to halt the process of perfecting nuclear arms and developing new weapons of that kind. The opportunity must not be missed. The Soviet proposals put the USSR and the United States in an equal position. These proposals are not an attempt to outwit or outsmart the other side. We propose embarking on a road of sensible and responsible decisions.

III

In order to implement the programme of reducing and eliminating nuclear arsenals, it is necessary to activate the entire existing system of negotiations and to ensure the highest possible efficiency of the disarmament mechanism.

In a few days the Soviet-American talks on nuclear and space arms will be resumed in Geneva. When we met with President Reagan last November in Geneva, we had a frank discussion on the whole range of problems which are the subject of those negotiations, namely on space, strategic offensive armaments and medium-range nuclear systems. It was agreed that the negotiations should be accelerated and this agreement must not remain a mere declaration.

The Soviet delegation in Geneva will be instructed to act in strict compliance with that agreement. We expect the same constructive approach from the US side, above all on the question of space. Space must remain peaceful, strike weapons must not be deployed there. Neither must they be developed. And there must also be introduced very strict control, including the opening of relevant laboratories for inspection.

Mankind is at a crucial stage of the new space age. And it is time to abandon the thinking of the stone age, when the chief concern was to have a bigger stick or a heavier stone. We are against weapons in space. Our material and intellectual capabilities make it possible for the Soviet Union to develop any weapon if we are compelled to do so. But we are fully aware of our responsibility to the present and future generations. It is our profound conviction that we should approach the third millennium not with the Star Wars programme, but with large-scale projects of peaceful space exploration by all mankind. We propose to start practical work in developing and implementing such projects. This is one of the most important ways of ensuring progress on our entire planet and establishing a reliable system of security for all.

To prevent the arms race from spreading to outer space means to remove the obstacle barring the way to drastic reductions in nuclear weapons. On the negotiating table in Geneva is a Soviet proposal to reduce by one half the corresponding nuclear arms of the Soviet Union and the United States, which would be an important step towards the complete elimination of nuclear weapons. To block all possibility of resolving the problem of space indicates a lack of desire to stop the arms race on earth. This should be stated in clear and straightforward terms. It is not by chance that the proponents of the nuclear arms race are also ardent supporters of the Star Wars programme. These are two sides of the same policy, hostile to the interests of people.

Let me turn to the European aspect of the nuclear problem. It is a matter of extreme concern that in defiance of reason and contrary to the national interests of the European peoples, American first-strike missiles continue to be deployed in certain West European countries. This problem has been under discussion for many years now. Meanwhile the security situation in Europe continues to deteriorate.

It is time to put an end to this course of events and cut this Gordian knot. The Soviet Union has long been proposing that Europe should be freed of both medium-range and tactical nuclear weapons. This proposal remains valid. As a first radical step in this direction we now propose, as I have said, that even at the first stage of our programme all medium-range ballistic and cruise missiles of the USSR and the USA in the European zone should be eliminated.

The achievement of tangible practical results at the Geneva talks would give meaningful material substance to our programme to eliminate nuclear arms completely by the year 2000.

IV

The Soviet Union considers the task of completely eliminating still in this century such barbaric weapons of mass destruction as chemical weapons fully feasible.

At the talks on chemical weapons within the framework of the Geneva Conference on Disarmament certain signs of progress have recently become evident. However, these talks have been inadmissibly drawn out. We are in favour of intensifying the talks on the conclusion of an effective and verifiable international convention prohibiting chemical weapons and destroying the existing stockpiles of those weapons, as was agreed upon with US President Reagan at Geneva.

In the matter of banning chemical weapons, as in other disarmament matters, all participants in the talks should take a fresh look at things. I would like to make it perfectly clear that the Soviet Union is in favour of prompt and complete elimination of those weapons and of the industrial base for their production. We are prepared to make a timely announcement of the location of enterprises producing chemical weapons and ensure the cessation of their production: we are ready to start developing procedures for destroying the corresponding industrial base and to proceed, soon after the convention enters into force, to eliminate the stockpiles of chemical weapons. All these measures would be carried out under strict control, including international on-site inspections.

A radical solution to this problem would also be facilitated by certain interim steps. For example, agreement could be reached on a multilateral basis not to transfer chemical weapons to anyone and not to deploy them in the territories of other states. As for the Soviet Union, it has always strictly abided by these principles in its practical policies. We call upon other states to follow this example and exercise equal restraint.

V

In addition to eliminating weapons of mass destruction from the arsenals of states, the Soviet Union proposes that conventional weapons and armed forces become subject to agreed-upon reductions.

Reaching an agreement at the Vienna negotiations could signal the beginning of progress in this direction. It now appears that an outline is discernable of a possible decision to reduce Soviet and US troops and subsequently freeze the level of armed forces of the opposing sides in Central Europe. The Soviet Union and our Warsaw Treaty allies are determined to achieve success at the Vienna talks. If the other side also truly wants this, 1986 could become a landmark for the Vienna talks too. We proceed from the understanding that a possible agreement on troop reductions would naturally require reasonable verification. We are prepared for this. As for observing the commitment to freeze the number of troops, in addition to national technical means permanent verification posts could be established to monitor any military contingents entering the reduction zone.

Let me now mention such an important forum as the Stockholm Conference on Confidence- and Security-Building Measures and Disarmament in Europe. It is called upon to create barriers against the use of force or covert preparations for war, whether on land, at sea or in the air. The possibilities for this have now become evident.

In our view, especially in the current situation, it is essential to reduce the number of troops participating in major military manoeuvres which are notifiable under the Helsinki Final Act.

It is time to begin dealing effectively with the problems still outstanding at the Conference. The bottleneck there, as we know, is the issue of notifications regarding major ground force, naval and air force exercises. Of course, these are serious problems and they must be addressed in a serious manner in the interests of building confidence in Europe. However, if their comprehensive solution cannot be achieved at this time, why not explore ways for partial solution, for instance reach an agreement now about notifications of major ground force and air force exercises, postponing the question of naval activities until the next stage of the Conference.

It is not by chance that a significant part of the new Soviet initiatives is addressed directly to Europe. Europe could play a special role in bringing about a radical turn towards the policy of peace. That role is to erect a new edifice of detente.

For this Europe has a necessary, often unique historical experience. Suffice it to recall that the joint efforts of the Europeans, the United States and Canada produced the Helsinki Final Act. If there is a need for a specific and vivid example of new thinking and political psychology in approaching the problems of peace, cooperation and international trust, that historic document could in many ways serve as such an example.

VI

Ensuring security in Asia is of vital importance to the Soviet Union, a major Asian power. The Soviet programme for eliminating nuclear and chemical weapons by the end of the current century is harmonious with the sentiments of the peoples of the Asian continent, for whom the problems of peace and security are no less urgent than for the peoples of Europe. In this context one cannot fail to recall that Japan and its cities of Hiroshima and Nagasaki became the victims of the nuclear bomb and Vietnam – a target for chemical weapons.

We highly appreciate the constructive initiatives put forward by the socialist countries of Asia, by India and other members of the non-aligned movement. We view as very important the fact that the two Asian nuclear powers, the USSR and the People's Republic of China, have undertaken a pledge not to be the first to use nuclear weapons.

The implementation of our programme would fundamentally change the situation in Asia, rid the nations in that part of the globe as well of the fear of nuclear and chemical warfare, bring security in that region to a qualitatively new level.

We see our programme as a contribution to a search, together with all the Asian countries, for an overall comprehensive approach to establishing a system of secure and lasting peace on this continent.

VII

Our new proposals are addressed to the entire world. Initiating active steps to halt the arms race and reduce weapons is a necessary prerequisite for coping with increasingly acute global problems – those of the deteriorating state of man's environment and of the need to find new energy sources and combat economic backwardness, hunger and disease. The pattern imposed by militarism – arms in place of development – must be replaced by the reverse order of things – disarmament for development. The noose of the trillion-dollar foreign debt, currently strangling dozens of countries and entire continents, is a direct consequence of the arms race. The more than 250,000 million dollars annually siphoned out of the developing countries is practically equal to the size of the mammoth US military budget. Indeed, this is no chance coincidence.

The Soviet Union wants each measure limiting and reducing arms and each step towards eliminating nuclear weapons not only to bring nations security but also to make it possible to allocate more funds for improving people's life. It is natural that the peoples seeking to put an end to backwardness and rise to the level of industrially developed countries associate the prospects of freeing themselves from the burden of foreign debt to imperialism, which is draining their economies, with limiting and eliminating weapons, reducing military expenditures and transferring resources to the goals of social and economic development. This subject will undoubtedly figure most prominently at the international conference on disarmament and development to be held in Paris next summer.

The Soviet Union is opposed to making the implementation of disarmament measures dependent on so-called regional conflicts. Behind this lie both an unwillingness to follow the path of disarmament and a desire to impose upon sovereign nations what is alien to them and a system that would make it possible to maintain profoundly unfair conditions whereby some countries live at the expense of others, exploiting their natural, human and intellectual resources for the selfish imperial purposes of individual states or aggressive alliances. The Soviet Union will continue as before to oppose this. It will continue consistently to advocate freedom for the peoples, peace, security, and a stronger international legal order. The Soviet Union's goal is not to whip up regional conflicts but to eliminate them through collective efforts on a just basis, and the sooner the better.

There is no shortage today of statements professing commitment to peace. What is in short supply are concrete actions to strengthen the foundations of peace. All too often peaceful words conceal war preparations and power politics. Moreover, some statements made from high rostrums are in fact intended to eliminate any trace of that new spirit of Geneva which is having a salutary effect on international relations today. It is not only a matter of statements. There are also actions clearly designed to incite animosity and mistrust, to revive confrontation, the antithesis of detente.

We reject such a way of acting and thinking. We want 1986 to be not just a peaceful year but one that will enable us to reach the end of the 20th century under the sign of peace and nuclear disarmament. The set of new foreign policy initiatives we are proposing is intended to make it possible for mankind to approach the year 2000 under peaceful skies and with a peaceful outer space, without fear of nuclear, chemical or any other threat of annihilation and fully confident of its own survival and of the continuation of the human race.

The new resolute measures being taken by the Soviet Union to defend peace and improve the overall international situation give expression to the substance and the spirit of our internal and foreign policies and their organic unity. They reflect the fundamental historic law which was emphasized by Vladimir Lenin. The whole world sees that our country is holding high the banner of peace, freedom and humanism which was raised over our planet by the Great October Revolution.

In questions of preserving peace and saving mankind from the threat of nuclear war, let no one remain indifferent or stand aloof. This concerns all and everyone. Each state, large or small, socialist or capitalist, has an important contribution to make. Every responsible political party, every public organization and every person can also make an important contribution.

No task is more urgent, more noble or humane, than that of uniting all efforts to achieve this lofty goal. This task must be accomplished by our generation, not shifted onto the shoulders of those who will succeed us. This is the imperative of our time. This, I would say, is the burden of historic responsibility for our decisions and actions in the time remaining until the beginning of the third millennium.

The course of peace and disarmament will continue to be pivotal in the foreign policy of the CPSU and the Soviet state. In actively pursuing this course, the Soviet Union is prepared to engage in wide-ranging cooperation with all those who proceed from positions of reason, good will and an awareness of the responsibility to ensure mankind's future – a future without wars or weapons.

Further Reading

Carter, Ashton B., *Directed Energy Missile Defense in Space* (Washington DC, US Congress Office of Technology Assessment, 1985)

Carter, Ashton B. and Schwartz, David, (eds) *Ballistic Missile Defense* (Washington DC, Brookings Institute, 1984)

Center for International Security and Arms Control, *Space Missile Defense; Necessities, Prospects and Dangers in the Near Term* (California, Stanford University, 1985)

Department of Defense, *Soviet Military Power* (Washington DC, 1985)

Department of Defense, *Soviet Strategic Defense Programs* (Washington DC, 1985)

Garwin, Richard L., Gottfried, Kurt, Kendall, Henry W., *The Fallacy of Star Wars* (New York, Random House, 1984)

Gray, Colin S., *Nuclear Strategy and Strategic Planning* (Philadelphia, Foreign Policy Research Institute, 1984)

Jastrow, Robert, *How to Make Nuclear Weapons Obsolete* (Boston MA, Little, Brown & Co, 1985)

The Whitehouse, *The President's Strategic Defense Initiative* (Washington DC, 1985)

Union of Concerned Scientists, *Ballistic Missile Defense* (Washington DC, 1984)

US Congress Office of Technology Assessment, *Anti-satellite Weapons, Countermeasures and Arms Control* (Washington DC, 1985)

US Congress Office of Technology Assessment, *Ballistic Missile Defense Technologies* (Washington DC, 1985)

Index